Flood risk management

Learning to live with rivers

Edited by
George Fleming

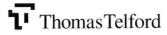 Thomas Telford

Published by Thomas Telford Publishing, Thomas Telford Ltd, 1 Heron Quay, London, E14 4JD

URL: http://www.thomastelford.com

Distributors for Thomas Telford books are
USA: ASCE Press, 1801 Alexander Bell Drive, Reston, VA 20191-4400, USA
Japan: Maruzen Co. Ltd, Book Department, 3–10 Nihonbashi 2-chome, Chuo-ku, Tokyo 103
Australia: DA Books and Journals, 648 Whitehorse Road, Mitcham 3132, Victoria

First published 2002

A catalogue record for this book is available from the British Library

ISBN: 0 7277 3112 2

© The Authors and Thomas Telford Limited, 2002

Typeset by Alex Lazarou, Surbiton, Surrey
Printed and bound in Great Britain by MPG Books, Bodmin, Cornwall

The Authors

Professor George Fleming FICE (Editor)
Past President of the Institution of Civil Engineers
Professor of Civil Engineering, University of Strathclyde, Glasgow

Mr Lindsay Frost MRTPI
Director of Planning and Environmental Services, Lewes District Council

Dr Stephen Huntingdon FICE
Managing Director, HR Wallingford Ltd

Professor Donald Knight MICE
Professor of Water Engineering, The University of Birmingham

Mr Frank Law FICE
Formerly Deputy Director, NERC Centre for Ecology and Hydrology Wallingford

Mr Charlie Rickard FICE
Director, Mott MacDonald Ltd

Support provided by

Dr Kenneth MacDougall (Technical Assistant)
Water Sector Manager, EnviroCentre Ltd

Ms Anne-Marie Ferguson (Secretary)
Institution of Civil Engineers

Additional support provided by

Ms Patricia Sheffield
Hydrologist, EnviroCentre Ltd

Foreword

Gary Kass and Marina Suleymanova,
Parliamentary Office of Science and Technology

Up to 5 million people in the UK are at risk from river and coastal flooding. Annual average damage is estimated at around £800 million (DTLR, 2001). Recent severe flooding has lead to suggestions that it is becoming more common and causing greater damage. While research continues on whether this trend is real, a number of possible causes are suggested — building on flood plains, alterations to river channels, changes in rainfall patterns and changes in agricultural and land management practice. Climate change is also predicted to increase flooding risk. This book outlines the policy and practice of managing flood risk, and examines questions over how the response might be improved.

BACKGROUND

River flooding is essentially a natural process that helps shape the landscape. It occurs when excessive rainfall (or melting snow) overwhelms the ability of the land to drain the water effectively. This is aggravated when the ground is already saturated, and when river channels become blocked by debris. Flooding is also exacerbated by changes in land use such as building in flood plains, and changes in agricultural practices.

Throughout history, flooding has threatened human life and property. There have been many significant river floods in the UK, with the most devastating in 1947, when nearly 700 000 acres of land was covered by flood water, affecting most of southern, eastern and central England. In 1953, 300 lives were lost and £5 billion of damage was caused by coastal flooding. These events prompted

Recent significant flooding in the UK

Easter 1998

The floods lasted six days and affected an area from Worcestershire to Cambridgeshire. More than 1500 people were evacuated, five people died (although there is a question over whether they died as a direct consequence of the floods), and £500–700 million of damage was caused.

Autumn 2000

Autumn 2000 was the wettest in the UK since records began (over 270 years ago) — much of the UK experienced prolonged and intense rainfall. For instance, rainfall in October was four times the average for the month. In that period, more than 10 000 properties were flooded in England and Wales, and nearly 300 000 were at risk of flooding. Widespread disruption to road and rail services occurred. Weather-related insurance claims totalled some £1 billion of damage.

changes in flood defence legislation and encouraged a substantial programme of building flood defences. The Easter 1998 and autumn 2000 floods (see box above) demonstrated that the risk remains significant.

A WORSENING PROBLEM?

In early 2001, the Commons Agriculture Select Committee noted (Commons Agriculture Select Committee, 2001) that the impacts of the 1998 and 2000 floods were lessened by previous investment, but pointed out that the potential impact of flooding on the nation's wealth and well-being is still significant, and potentially growing for a number of reasons

- many flood defences will reach the end of their operating capacity over the next decade

- the Government's estimates for new homes may increase pressure to develop on flood plains
- climate change will affect rainfall patterns (on coastal flooding, sea levels are expected to rise by up to 6 mm each year over the next 50 years in south-east England), so increasing the risk of inland flooding.

POLICY FRAMEWORK

Government policy on flooding (see box below) is to reduce risks to people, property and the environment by

- encouraging the use of adequate and cost-effective flood warning systems
- encouraging economically, technically and environmentally sound flood defence measures
- discouraging inappropriate development in areas at risk from flooding and coastal erosion.

Responsibilities for flooding policy

Flooding policy is fully devolved, as follows

- England — the Department for the Environment, Food and Rural Affairs (DEFRA)
- Scotland — the Scottish Executive Environment and Rural Affairs Department
- Wales — the National Assembly for Wales
- Northern Ireland — the Department of the Environment.

On flooding, the United Kingdom parliament has jurisdiction only in England. DEFRA sets the criteria for investment priorities, pays capital grants to 'operating authorities', funds a research programme; and ensures dissemination of best practice. In April 2000, DEFRA (then the Ministry of Agriculture, Fisheries and Food (MAFF)) set a series of 'high-level targets' for the operating authorities against which it could monitor achievement of its aims and objectives for flood defence. The targets include (among others)

- providing policy statements setting out plans for delivering flood defence policy aims and objectives
- providing warnings and running emergency exercises
- developing a national database, through inspections of flood defences and flood risk assessments
- producing reports on development in flood risk areas.

Who implements policy?
This is the responsibility of 'operating authorities'.

- The *Environment Agency* is the principal operating authority in England and Wales (the Rivers Agency in Northern Ireland and the lead role is taken by the local authorities in Scotland). The Environment Agency carries out general supervision over all matters relating to flood defence. It implements programmes of capital, maintenance and operational works, advises planning authorities on development and flood risk, reduces the risks of flooding from designated 'main rivers', carries out flood forecasting and issues flood warnings.
- There are 235 *internal drainage boards* in England and Wales which have permissible powers to carry out flood defence works on watercourses in their district, which are not designated as 'main river'.
- *Local authorities* in England and Wales undertake flood defence works on watercourses not designated as 'main river' and outside internal drainage boards' districts.
- In addition, a large number of flood defences are privately owned and maintained, for example by the Highways Agency, Railtrack, and other land owners.

APPROACHES TO MANAGING FLOODS

Flood defences are built to protect people's lives and property and to sustain economic activity. Flood defences cannot provide absolute protection against all possible flooding, but they can *reduce* the risk of flooding. Building defences to very high standards may be very expensive, may be highly intrusive in the human and natural environment and may actually increase risks elsewhere or have disastrous results if any part of the system fails. Thus, there needs to be a balance between all costs and benefits. This is assisted by a range of indicative 'standards of protection' (see box below) that aim to ensure that risks are reduced to a level that is appropriate for the use of the land protected.

There is a wide range of technologies that can be applied for flood defence; their actual use being a decision based on balancing economic, environmental and social factors (see the later discussion of appraisal). The most common approaches seek to protect the

---

Standards of protection for flood defence

Severe floods occur less frequently than modest floods, leading to the idea of a flood having a 'return period', i.e. the number of years that might be expected between floods of a given size. For example, in some areas, the floods experienced in autumn 2000 would have been expected only once in 200 years. This of course does not mean that such an event will occur on a regular cycle, once every 200 years, but that, averaged over a long time period, an occurrence of this scale is likely. Indeed the risk is the same in any year.

It is not possible to protect against all floods, and so measures are taken according to the expected frequency of specific floods. For river flooding, this 'standard of protection' is often set at the level of the 1 in 100 year return period flood. This is also referred to as the '1 in 100 chance' flood, or the flood with 1% probability of occurrence in an individual year.

---

developed and natural environment by means of constructed defences, for example

- *raised river-banks and flood walls* — these exclude flood waters from the adjacent land and property but increase the height of flood waters above those protected areas
- *canalisation* (or chanellisation) is the straightening, deepening and widening of natural river channels to increase flow capacity and to reduce flood levels but this may have adverse impacts on areas downstream and will significantly affect the river's natural features
- *storage reservoirs* are used to regulate the flow of water in a main river channel by redirecting flood waters to a holding area and allowing the water to flow back into the main channel after the flood. Once the storage capacity has been exceeded, additional flood flows may continue downstream undiminished
- *sluices and barriers* are used to control and regulate the flow of water down the river channel — tidal barrages in estuaries prevent surges moving upstream.

Less common (but increasingly sought), are approaches that seek to enhance the natural capacity of a flood plain to store water, and to increase the amount of rainfall that can be absorbed into the soil higher up the catchment. Examples include maintaining meanders in river valleys, providing areas for floodwater storage (often also increasing nature conservation value), and ensuring sympathetic land management practices. These techniques are relatively novel, and there is less evidence of their cost-effectiveness than for the more traditional constructed defences.

ISSUES

Ensuring adequate funding

The Government's aim is to direct the funds available to areas of greatest priority. At present, annual investment in flood (and coastal defence) is around £400 million per year. Of this, £240 million is controlled by the Environment Agency (£150 million for capital works and £90 million for maintenance). Over the period 2000/01 to 2003/04, funding for capital works investment will have increased by

50%. However, it is widely recognised (e.g. by DEFRA (2001), the National Audit Office (NAO, 2001), the Environment Agency (2001a), and the Institution of Civil Engineers (ICE, 2001)) that a substantially higher level of investment is required to avoid deterioration from current levels of protection.

Moreover, there are indications (Osborn *et al.*, 2001) that climate change may have already increased winter rainfall over the UK, so potentially increasing flood risk. Estimates by DEFRA's consultants suggest that possible climate change would require investment to maintain current levels of protection to increase by £30–60 million per year.

ENSURING VALUE FOR MONEY

Towards a more strategic approach

Over the past two decades, there has been a greater acknowledgement of the impact of flooding on people and property but also recognition that building flood defences can have adverse economic and environmental effects. For instance, DEFRA, the NAO, the Environment Agency and the ICE have all stated that the costs of some flood defences can be out of proportion to the risks faced, can harm the environment, can make flooding worse in other locations and affect the appearance of a local area.

Underpinning these changes in approach, the NAO, the ICE, the Environment Agency and DEFRA point to a need for a long-term policy on flood defences that considers entire river catchment areas. Such 'catchment flood management plans' (CFMPs) are still in their infancy. Five pilot CFMPs are currently being developed by the Environment Agency (the Irwell, Derwent, Medway, Severn and Parrett catchments).

As an expression of these ideas, recent Government policy guidance (DTLR, 2001) seeks to influence developments in flood risk areas by stating

- no development, including flood defence schemes, should lead to an increased risk of flooding elsewhere
- the susceptibility of land to flooding is an important planning consideration
- policies in development plans should outline the consideration that will be given to flood issues

- development planning should, wherever possible, avoid flood risk, and always seek to manage appropriately
- inappropriate development on undeveloped and undefended flood plains should be avoided
- developers should fund flood defences and warning measures in flood risk areas.

PROJECT APPRAISAL

Recent reviews have highlighted the need for individual flood defence schemes to be assessed in the wider context of the river catchment. The Government, the Environment Agency, the NAO and the ICE recognise that these appraisals should take account of economic, environmental and social issues. Particular concerns are expressed by the ICE that the traditional appraisal of flood defence schemes has concentrated on mainly economic factors and so tends to overlook the consequences of flooding for affected people, especially in terms of the considerable distress and health damage that can result. For example, the ICE pointed out that houses often flood with sewage from drains and sewers overwhelmed by heavy rain. It suggests that this is more distressing than flooding from rivers and poses a considerable health risk. Such findings are supported by surveys by the Middlesex University Flood Hazard Research Centre (FHRC) of people's experiences from the 1998 floods.

The ICE therefore recommended that 'research be progressed to improve benefit-cost assessment, to enable monetary values to be attributed to the cost of health and social distress caused by flooding, or the benefit of its avoidance' (ICE, 2001). DEFRA has commissioned a research consortium, including the FHRC, to develop a methodology by which such 'human cost' can be readily brought into the appraisal framework, and the results should be available in 2003.

In May 2001, DEFRA published the latest volumes of guidance on appraising flood and coastal defence projects (see the box opposite). This provides advice on best practice for the appraisal of flood and coastal defence projects to ensure better use of public money and more transparent decision-making. Overall, the guidance points out that appraisals should take account of economic, environmental and technical issues underpinned with an adequate consideration of risk.

The appraisal of flood defence projects

Economic appraisal

The aim is to maximise overall protection through the national investment programme. Projects must demonstrate economic efficiency, so the standards of protection must be appropriate to the current land use. Projects are considered economically viable only if benefits exceed costs with the return on investment maximised where the highest ratio of benefits to costs can be demonstrated for each project by considering different options (including the 'do nothing' option), set against indicative standards.

Handling risk

Explicit account should be taken of uncertainties in the decision-making process. Where risks are identified they can be avoided by alternative approaches or managed to reduce their consequences.

Environmental appraisal

The guidance sets out the scope of the environmental aspects of flood defence (e.g. biodiversity and landscape). It recognises the difficulties of placing reliable monetary values on environmental impacts while offering advice for appraising common situations.

Other issues are included in the guidance, such as strategic planning, climate change and sustainability. DEFRA is planning to issue further guidance on evaluating the performance of projects once implemented.

INCREASING AWARENESS AND PREPAREDNESS

Flood forecasting and warning

The consequences of the 1998 Easter floods were summarised in the first box. A review of these events led (among other things) to the establishment of the Environment Agency's National Flood Warning Centre to develop flood forecasting and warning systems.

Flood forecasting involves interpreting measured and forecast rainfall, and river and tidal levels, often using sophisticated mathematical models. This requires monitoring systems, which consist of a network of rain and river flow gauges and associated systems supervised by the Environment Agency. Daily rainfall forecasts provide information on the likely quantities, distribution and timing of rain for up to five days ahead. In particular, heavy rainfall warnings issued for periods up to 24 hours ahead are used to assist flood forecasters in deciding when to issue flood warnings.

Weather radar can be used to estimate actual rainfall and, by extrapolating rainfall patterns, to support short-term forecasting. Forecasting methods vary from simple extrapolation of upstream river levels to predict levels at given points downstream, through to sophisticated predictive catchment flow forecasting modelling systems. While such models are useful in supporting decisions to issue flood warnings, the ICE points out that these remain very uncertain. Although research is continuing to improve forecasts, decisions to issue flood warnings remain a matter of human judgement.

EMERGENCY RESPONSE

The NAO, Environment Agency and the ICE have stated that the wide range of organisations and responsibilities involved creates difficulties and confusion, possibly even increasing the risk of suffering flood damage for some people. One option put forward (e.g. by the NAO and the ICE) is for the responsibilities to be firmly consolidated on a single executive agency with enhanced supervisory powers over the various operating authorities. The Government also plans to overhaul emergency planning legislation but the timetable is unclear at present.

CLEAN UP AND RECOVERY

As discussed above, flooding has a devastating effect on property and also causes great distress to the people affected. The Environment Agency has produced guidance on how to clean up, dry out, restore and repair a home after flooding, together with details of organisations that can offer information, support and practical help in the clean-up operation.

Clearly, however, the clean up has to be paid for. This is the role of flood insurance. The Association of British Insurers has stated that insurers wish to continue providing affordable cover against the risk of flood damage unless the risk has increased such that flooding has become inevitable (Association of British Insurers, 2000).

Glossary

Catchment	The land area that drains into a river
Catchment flood management plan	A large-scale planning document that identifies long-term sustainable policies for the holistic management of flood risks in a defined river catchment or group of related catchments
Consequence	An outcome or impact from a risk, which may be an economic, social or environmental impact
Critical ordinary watercourses	Ordinary watercourses which the Environment Agency and other operating authorities agree are critical because they have the potential to put large numbers of people and property at risk from flooding
Benefit-cost ratio	The ratio of the present value of benefits to the present value of costs
Exposure	The period during which a risk can be realised
Flood	Great flow of water causing overflow and inundation

Flood risk assessment	Consideration of risks inherent in flooding
Hazard	A situation with the potential to result in harm. A hazard does not necessarily lead to harm
Hydrology	The study of water resources
Hydraulics	The application of fluid mechanics principles to natural channels or engineered structures
Hydrodynamics	The study of fluids in motion
Intangible	Describes those costs, benefits and risks that are difficult to quantify but which are, nevertheless, relevant for the decision-making process. Usually applied to non-monetary impacts, such as households that do not have direct financial impacts
Main river	Watercourse designated as such on main river maps and are generally larger arterial watercourses
Ordinary watercourses/ non-main rivers	Those watercourses not designated as 'main river'
Pathway	The means by which the source can impact a receptor
Probability	The odds against a certain event happening in any year, expressed either in gaming terminology (e.g. the 100 to 1 flood), or as a percentage (e.g. the 1% flood). All things being equal, the odds remain the same each year, regardless of any recent severe occurrences

Receptor	The target that will be threatened by harm from the hazard
Risk	A combination of the probability and frequency of occurrence of harm being realised from a hazard
Risk management	The activity of mitigating and monitoring risks, which predominantly occurs after the project appraisal phase
Source	The initial condition that can lead to a hazard and subsequent risk being realised
Vulnerability	The extent to which a hazard poses a risk to a receptor

Abbreviations

CEHW   Centre for Ecology and Hydrology Wallingford (formerly Institute of Hydrology)

DEFRA   Department for the Environment, Food and Rural Affairs (formerly MAFF)

DTLR   Department for Transport, Local Government and the Regions

EPSRC   Engineering and Physical Sciences Research Council

EU   European Union

ICE   Institution of Civil Engineers

MAFF   Ministry for Agriculture, Fisheries and Food (now DEFRA)

NERC   Natural Environment Research Council

OFWAT   Office of Water Services

SUDS   Sustainable urban drainage systems

Contents

1 Flooding and flood estimation

George Fleming and Lindsay Frost

A flood is a 'great flow of water, causing overflow and inundation' (*Chambers*, 1981). Floods are natural events resulting from high rainfall, and can be made worse as a result of land use changes (e.g. from meadow to housing estate or from rough pasture to arable cropping). Flood damage is usually the consequence of man's activities in areas at risk from flooding (see Figure 1.1).

1.1 HISTORIC DEVELOPMENT OF FLOOD PLAINS

Settlements have always been sited on flood plains, despite the risk of periodic flooding. Historically, these risks have been outweighed by the many social, economic and environmental benefits of a riverside location (Figure 1.2).

The social and economic benefits arise mainly from the trading advantages of sites at river crossing points, along valley routes, or at transhipment points between river or sea transport and inland routes. In addition, riverside sites were often militarily defensible, providing good sites for castles and other fortifications.

Environmentally, flood plain sites were often the most fertile and workable agricultural land. They also offered sustainable sources of water power for economic activities, such as milling, tanning and brewing.

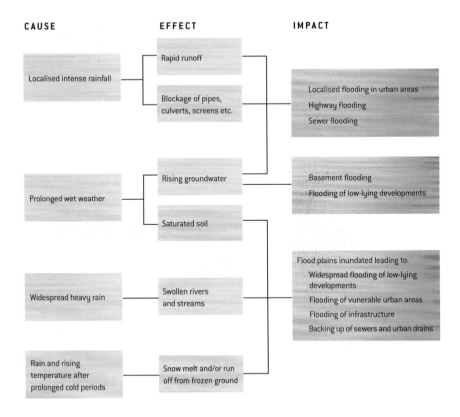

CAUSE   EFFECT   IMPACT

Localised intense rainfall — Rapid runoff / Blockage of pipes, culverts, screens etc. → Localised flooding in urban areas / Highway flooding / Sewer flooding

Prolonged wet weather — Rising groundwater / Saturated soil → Basement flooding / Flooding of low-lying developments

Widespread heavy rain — Swollen rivers and streams → Flood plains inundated leading to: Widespread flooding of low-lying developments / Flooding of vunerable urban areas / Flooding of infrastructure / Backing up of sewers and urban drains

Rain and rising temperature after prolonged cold periods — Snow melt and/or run off from frozen ground

Figure 1.1. The many causes, effects and impacts of inland flooding

Almost all the ancient towns and cities of England and Wales have locations alongside rivers, with some properties vulnerable to flooding (e.g. London, York, Winchester, Norwich, Exeter, Oxford, Cambridge, Carlisle, Chester, Gloucester, Worcester, Shrewsbury).

The social and economic advantages of flood plain locations were consolidated by the industrial revolution from the late 18th century onwards, with much industrial development, and accompanying workers' housing, being based on river, canal and railway routes along river valleys.

Rivers are still an economic asset for towns, even though very little commercial river traffic remains. Rivers are often an important element in the tourism 'offer' of towns and cities (e.g. Cambridge) and the focus of their regeneration efforts (e.g. Leeds and Gloucester).

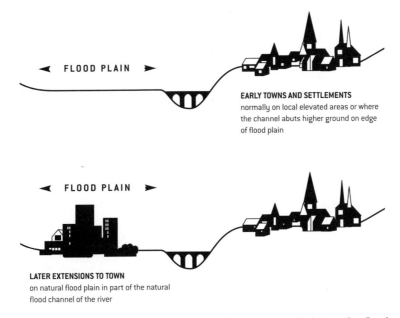

Figure 1.2. Many riverside settlements have encroached into the flood plain

1.2 EFFECT OF HISTORIC TOWNS ON FLOOD RISK MANAGEMENT

Many centuries of development in riverside towns has involved construction of structures affecting the dynamics of river flow and associated flood risk. These structures include bridges, river walls and embankments, and historic flood defences. Sometimes these structures can combine to catastrophic effect, with old bridges acting as 'choke points' for river flows, leading to a build-up of a head of water behind them and massive overtopping of river walls. This happened on the River Ouse in Lewes in the Autumn 2000 floods (Figure 1.3).

There are also structures outside the historic core of riverside towns that can affect river hydraulics and cause flooding in historic areas. These include road causeways and railway embankments. Normally, these are essential parts of transport infrastructure. However, in flood conditions, they can reduce the volume of storage space available on

Flood plain development: Tonbridge

Many towns suffer from 'people creep' onto the flood plain. Tonbridge is a striking example, which is far from rare. It developed before the 20th century as two communities up the valley sides that were linked by a bridge crossing but gave space for the flood plain vagaries of the River Medway. Navigation was created as far back as 1750 to link Tonbridge to the sea, but only the business pressures of the last 100 years saw encroachment onto the land at risk (Figure 1.2). Shops, commerce, factories and industrial facilities (such as the sewage works) dominated, suggesting that common sense had some influence within the planning process.

The September 1968 flood, coming after a few decades of more modest floods, was a rude awakening and led to the subsequent construction of the Leigh Barrier storage 'washland' immediately upstream of the town. This structure, designed to suppress any flood smaller than the 1% annual probability of flooding, proved its worth in the autumn 2000 floods. Arguably if it had been built before 'people creep' it would have been an excellent economic growth investment for the town. However, it has to be remembered by all who live and work there that when (not 'if') a flood greater than the 100 to 1 flood occurs there will be no protection other than a few hours extra warning to evacuate.

the flood plain or channel water more quickly towards historic areas. Conversely, such structures can be helpful by providing something akin to secondary flood defences in some circumstances.

Historic towns often have a legacy of ancient drainage infrastructure comprising ditches, culverts and drains, often now built over with later development. Where such infrastructure fails to function (e.g. because of blockages) and contributes to flooding problems, legal responsibility for maintenance is often unclear, and no one party is keen to take it on. This problem is compounded by the legal responsibilities of each party being based on permissive powers rather than statutory duties.

Figure 1.3. Features such as bridges in historic towns can lead to 'choke points' which are prone to water buid-up upstream and subsequent overtopping

Where floodwater enters an historic area, particularly where flood defences are breached or overtopped and flooding happens quickly, the dense pattern of building coverage and narrow streets and alleyways can significantly increase the speed and level of flooding. The velocity of flood water may also increase, adding to potential damage to historic buildings, walls and other structures.

A special problem for some historic towns, particularly in the chalk land of southern England (e.g. Chichester, Winchester, Salisbury and Romsey) is groundwater-fed flooding. After prolonged and heavy rainfall, groundwater levels can rise to the point where widespread flooding can occur from intermittent streams, springs and rising groundwater. In some ways, it can be more difficult to manage than river flooding, requiring extensive diversionary action, such as employed in Chichester in the autumn and winter of 2000/1.

The scope for flood alleviation works in historic towns is constrained by their special character. This may make flood defences more difficult, or expensive, to provide if they are to be successfully assimilated into the historic environment. The problems of assimilation also extend to the design of new buildings, and adaptation of existing buildings, to offset flood risk. Here raised floor levels, provision of sustainable urban drainage systems (SUDS) infrastructure and compensating flood storage, and retro-fitting of flood resistant products can all present design problems.

Shrewsbury, a historic town on the River Severn has a long record of flooding (Environment Agency, 2001b). During the early 1990s a flood defence scheme was proposed for the town by the National Rivers Authority. However, the effect on the appearance of the historic town centre was considered unacceptable and the scheme did not proceed. Following further flooding in autumn 2000, a fresh scheme has been prepared by the Environment Agency that includes some demountable defences.

It is important to recognise that the historical towns are only a part of the flooding problem. Recent developments in the last half century have seen the construction of large areas of new housing and commercial facilities together with the expansion of infrastructure including the road, rail and airport networks. Agriculture and forestry have intensified as have the pressure on our river systems to provide more water resources and to provide increased drainage.

The two main factors affecting floods, the meteorology and the physical conditions in the river basin, have both varied significantly in the recent past.

1.3 EARLY FLOOD ESTIMATION

Engineers have faced the problem of flood flow estimation throughout the ages and have, in general, treated it subjectively, designing intuitively for the largest known flood.

The earliest flood mark in the UK is thought to be the 1607 tidal incursion of the Bristol Channel into the Somerset Levels. However, the majority of flood records in the UK do not begin until the 17th century — and these record only the peak level that the river reached, not the actual volume of water being discharged. The longest known flow record in the UK is that of Wendover Springs, dating from 1841. Flow was routinely measured on the Lee and Thames from the 1880s, but the majority of the river flow records available in the UK are relatively short. Gauging stations only became widespread in the 1950s when the full utility of flow records was realised (Figure 1.4).

The industrial revolution was a time of scientific development and people were beginning to question the myth that streams were fed by underground channels with water capacities far in excess of that available through rainfall. In 1674, a French scientist, Perrault, measured the rainfall in the Seine river basin and then estimated the runoff. This was the first recorded quantitative experiment into rainfall–runoff relationships (Biswas, 1967).

The first logical attempts to estimate flood flows were made in the 1840s. The result was the development of the rational method, which was presented to the Institute of Engineers in Ireland (Mulvaney, 1850). This method links river flow to the size of the catchment, the intensity of rainfall falling in a given time and a coefficient of runoff, the value of which is catchment dependent. The rational method remains valid today and provides a reasonable estimate of river flow for a given rainfall event. It is, however, highly dependent on the choice of runoff coefficient.

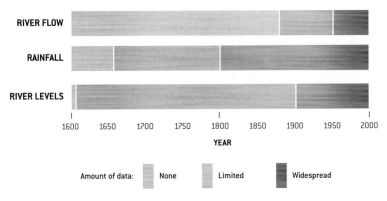

Figure 1.4. Most river flow (as opposed to river level) data are less than 50 years old

The late 19th and early 20th century marked the development of a spate of empirical rainfall–runoff relationships, all incorporating a catchment-dependent factor. Although the maximum historic flood generally provided more realistic peak flows for design criteria, empirical methods were favoured due to the increasing availability of historic rainfall data.

1.3.1 Early 20th century developments

There was no published guidance for engineers designing structures affected by flood flows until the Reservoir (Safety Provision) Act 1930 placed a statutory obligation on reservoir owners that all reservoirs with a capacity in excess of 5 million gallons (22·7 million litres) should be subject to inspection in the interests of public safety.

The 1930 Act resulted from problems previously experienced with the failure of reservoirs in flood conditions. In particular, the weakening of impounding earth embankments due to erosion from overflowing water had resulted in several reservoir failures, leading to major flooding downstream, significant loss of life and damage to property. Following this Act, the Institution of Civil Engineers (ICE) produced a report on floods in relation to reservoir practice in 1933.

The terms of reference for the ICE's 1933 report were 'to examine the present state of knowledge in regard to the magnitude of floods in relation to reservoir practice in Great Britain and to make recommendations on the best methods of dealing with them in that connection'.

The approach recommended was flood peaks based on drainage area. This method relied on plotting existing recorded floods against catchment area to form an enveloping curve for the normal maximum floods. Two curves were presented for upland catchments, depending on whether they were greater than or less than 25 000 acres (10 118 hectares). Further provision was included for the occurrence of rare but exceptional rainfall events, causing the unfortunately termed 'acute catastrophic floods'. Since no such events had been recorded, the committee felt that a reasonable design criterion was to assume that exceptional peak flows would be double those experienced during normal maximum floods. This publication was a major step towards standardising design practice across the country, and it was refined and republished not long after the Lynmouth flood disaster in 1952.

1.3.2 The advent of statistical methods

To manage flood risk successfully, knowledge is needed of both the magnitude of any given flood and an estimate of the likelihood of this flood occurring.

By the 1920s scientists and engineers were beginning to consider the application of probability theory in estimating stream flow. Various types of probability-distribution curves were developed, all essentially using existing flow records to assign a probability of occurrence to a given flow value. These statistical methods relied on the length of record and the quality of available flow data. Such methods assume that each recorded flow is part of an independent dataset — but obviously this is not the case, with one day's flow being heavily influenced by conditions the previous day and also by seasonality and long-term climate trends. This condition of independence is achieved approximately by considering only the maximum flow for each water year to form an 'independent' series of annual peaks.

Statistical methods based on previous flooding experience are fine if the catchment is gauged so that an assessment of flood risk can be made based on previous experience. However, many catchments are not gauged and an assessment of flood risk must be based on knowledge of a design storm. This approach uses the relationship between rainfall and runoff to produce a flood 'hydrograph' — a plot of water flow against time — taking into account the areal extent, depth and duration of the rainfall event and the losses and time lags expected between rainfall and runoff. The 'unit hydrograph' is used as a standard, which is the hydrograph of surface runoff resulting from effective rainfall falling in a unit time and falling uniformly in space and time across the catchment. Both the statistical and unit hydrograph approaches are useful tools in estimating the risk of potential floods. It must be noted, however, they are only linear approximations and do not represent dynamic variations of storm distribution or changes in land use.

1.4 THE *FLOOD STUDIES REPORT*

By 1965 the field of 'flood protection' engineering was expanding and the ICE held a symposium on river flood hydrology to assess existing methods. It was felt that frequency analysis methods were only being used when the budget of the project was large enough to justify the work involved and that, for smaller projects, a variety of methods were being used to produce discharge estimates. A need for a reliable and universal method, applicable to both large and small schemes, was required.

In the United States the US Geological Survey had been developing the regional flood frequency method, combining the flow records of a group of stations in a hydrologically homogeneous area to obtain a longer record and, thus, reduce the sampling error. This method was widely accepted in the US and offered significant improvements to flood risk analysis in the UK. Regional frequency curves were produced for England and Wales (Cole, 1965) and Scotland (Biswas and Fleming, 1966).

During the 1960s several major flooding events occurred throughout the UK, in particular the 1968 floods in the Bristol region and south-east England caused widespread chaos and distress, and this gave the Government the impetus to commission the *Flood Studies Report* (NERC, 1975), a formal review of flood estimation techniques in use in the UK.

The primary aim of the 1975 report was to recommend flood estimation techniques, based on statistics derived from available hydrological, meteorological and topographical information, for use by practising engineers to address land drainage and flood protection problems. Another aim was to provide guidance on the treatment of flat low-lying catchments, which remained un-addressed in the previous guidelines on reservoir safety.

The two main approaches endorsed by the 1975 report were

- statistical frequency analysis of peak flows
- development of a unit hydrograph corresponding to a design storm and catchment characteristics.

If details on the shape and volume of the flood or an estimate of the maximum flood were required, as opposed to flows for given probabilities, then the unit hydrograph approach was recommended. The weakness of the 1975 report was that it relied heavily on existing data and made no attempt to estimate future extreme events. Furthermore, it did not take account of changes in land use patterns, such as significant urbanisation. Thus, it offers a static view of flood estimation.

As can be seen from Figure 1.5, the 1960s regional frequency curve of Biswas and Fleming (1966) is comparable with that of the 1975 recommendations.

At the time of the Reservoirs Act 1975, the ICE was readdressing its guidelines and published *Floods and Reservoir Safety — an Engineering Guide* in 1978. This addressed the changes in legislation brought in by the Reservoirs Act 1975, which changed the statutory criterion for compliance to reservoirs with a capacity in excess of 25

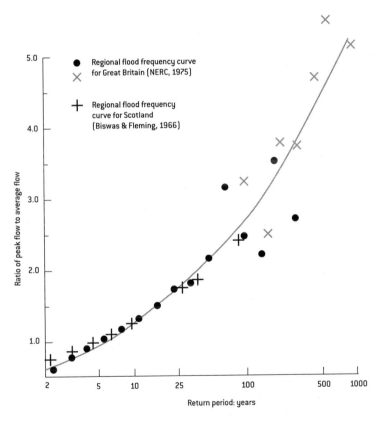

Figure 1.5. Regional flood frequency curves produced for Scotland in 1966 and Great Britain in 1975

Flood frequency calculation for the 100–1 chance flood for the River Clyde at Daldowie

(Using the Gringorten Method for annual maxima as recommended in the *Flood Studies Report*)

Date	Q	Rank	$P(X)$	$F(X)$	$T(x)$
22/09/85	755·2	1	0·02	0·98	46·64
30/10/77	739·6	2	0·06	0·94	16·74
14/08/66	613·1	3	0·10	0·90	10·20
04/01/82	574·8	4	0·14	0·86	7·34
24/11/63	536·0	5	0·17	0·83	5·73
03/12/99	515·4	6	0·21	0·79	4·70
26/11/79	491·5	7	0·25	0·75	3·98
09/10/67	486·0	8	0·29	0·71	3·46
25/10/00	475·3	9	0·33	0·67	3·05
02/01/81	454·9	10	0·37	0·63	2·73
30/12/86	438·9	11	0·40	0·60	2·47
11/02/98	430·9	12	0·44	0·56	2·26
31/10/70	415·3	13	0·48	0·52	2·08
22/02/70	406·7	14	0·52	0·48	1·93
07/10/64	391·0	15	0·56	0·44	1·79
18/01/74	387·4	16	0·60	0·40	1·68
21/12/85	381·6	17	0·63	0·37	1·58
16/11/78	360·3	18	0·67	0·33	1·49
19/12/66	358·8	19	0·71	0·29	1·41
02/02/88	356·4	20	0·75	0·25	1·34
03/02/77	322·2	21	0·79	0·21	1·27
20/01/76	318·4	22	0·83	0·17	1·21
22/01/75	310·9	23	0·86	0·14	1·16
12/12/72	278·5	24	0·90	0·10	1·11
01/11/69	271·1	25	0·94	0·06	1·06
08/04/72	223·6	26	0·98	0·02	1·02

Gringorten Formula

$$P(X) = \left(\frac{r - 0.44}{N + 0.12} \right)$$

where $P(X)$ is the probability of exceedance, r is the ranking (descending), N is the number of annual maxima, and

$$F(X) = 1 - P(X), \quad \text{the probability of occurrence}$$

$$T(X) = \frac{1}{P(X)}, \quad \text{the return period}$$

From the flood frequency plot, the 100–1 chance flood or 1% probability flood for the River Clyde at Daldowie is found to be 830 m^3s^{-1} (Figure 1.6).

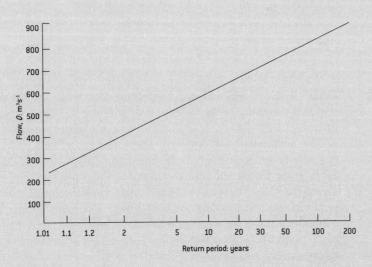

Figure 1.6. Flood frequency gumbel plot for the Clyde at Daldowie

million litres, and also tried to reduce the engineering community's subjectivity in interpreting the guidelines. The ICE's 1978 guide provided engineering guidelines for the design and operation of dams anywhere in Britain, whereas the 1975 *Flood Studies Report* provided wider guidance on a range of flood issues.

1.5   THE *FLOOD ESTIMATION HANDBOOK*

Both the 1975 *Flood Studies Report* and the 1978 *Floods and Reservoir Safety* guide aimed to provide an accurate assessment of flood risk in order to maximise public protection. Together they formed the cornerstones of flood risk assessment in the UK, until the publication and launch of the *Flood Estimation Handbook* in 1999 by the Institute of Hydrology, now the Centre for Ecology and Hydrology Wallingford (CEHW, 1999).

The *Flood Estimation Handbook* provides up-to-date guidelines on flood estimation and advice on estimating the rarity of rainfall events. As with the 1975 *Flood Studies Report*, the two primary methods recommended are

- statistical analysis of existing flow records
- rainfall–runoff methods utilising the unit hydrograph.

The rainfall–runoff method is as in the 1975 report with minor modifications. Regional analysis techniques have shifted from a regional grouping to the selection of catchments considered to be hydrologically similar, regardless of their geographic location.

The 2000 handbook does not take advantage of data collected in the more recent past. Peaks over threshold flows are only included up to the early 1980s and annual maximum flows are included only to the early 1990s. The wealth of useful data recorded in the past decade is not utilised in the derivation of regional curves. The handbook continues to be a steady-state method, estimating a fixed magnitude and probability without accounting for changes in river catchment or future extremes of weather.

In the last century, our understanding and ability to predict the magnitude and frequency of future flood events has increased greatly, providing engineers and planners with the information needed to plan flood protection and flood alleviation schemes. However, the widespread devastation caused by the floods of 1998 and 2000, following other localised occurrences, show that we still have a long way to go in providing the public with adequate flood risk management. This is partly a matter of funding. A sustained programme of investment in both existing and new flood defences is needed, as is investment in the development of more accurate methods of flood estimation and forecasting.

All flood estimation studies should follow the *Flood Estimation Handbook* (CEHW, 1999) maxims for flood frequency estimation.

1. Flood frequency is best estimated from gauged data.
2. Flood data at the subject site are most useful, however, data transfers from a nearby site, or similar catchment, are also useful.
3. Estimation of key variables from catchment descriptors alone should only be used as a last resort. Data transfer is usually feasible and is preferable.
4. While the appropriate choice of method is a function of experience, the requirements of the study and the nature of the catchment, the overriding factor is data availability.
5. In some cases a combination of statistical and rainfall-runoff methods will be appropriate.
6. There is always more information. An estimate based on readily available data may be shown to be suspect by a more enquiring analyst.

Training and experience is of vital importance in flood estimation and all studies should provide an audit trail including the following.

1. A clear method statement, defining the objectives of the study.

2. Documentation of all decisions.
3. Documentation of all data, calculations and computer printout.
4. Summary of results.
5. Review by appropriate staff member.

The Environment Agency have developed various pro-forma and checklists to assist in flood estimation. These provide a step-by-step guide to carrying out flood estimations, and should be used in conjunction with the *Flood Estimation Handbook*. The basic procedures to be followed are illustrated in Figure 1.7, and provide guidance on the most appropriate methods for use, dependent on data availability and the objectives of the study.

Other points worth noting are as follows (based on the Environment Agency's *Flood Estimation Guidelines* (Environment Agency, 2000c).

- Statistical methods are suitable for return periods of between 2–200 years.
- Rainfall-runoff methods, in conjunction with the *Flood Estimation Handbook* rainfall, are valid for return periods of up to 2000 years. However, such methods should not be used for catchments in excess of 1000 km^2.
- The data included with the *Flood Estimation Handbook* are not completely up-to-date and more recent data should be obtained wherever possible.
- It is always important to review all the available data.
- Catchment descriptors should always be treated with caution and flood estimates should not be made based on these for flood plain developments or locations where flooding is likely to cause fatalities.
- The *Flood Estimation Handbook* is only applicable to catchments less than 0·5 km^2 if gauged data are available.
- Extra care and consideration should be taken when catchments contain reservoirs or are affected by pumping or regulation.

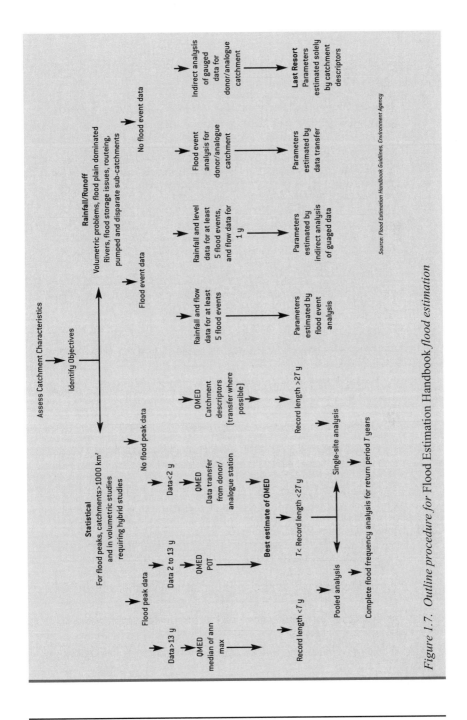

Figure 1.7. Outline procedure for Flood Estimation Handbook *flood estimation*

Flood frequency calculation for the 100–1 chance flood for the River Kelvin at Killermont

(Using the *Flood Estimation Handbook* rainfall–runoff method)

Grid Reference NS 558 705

This method is for use when no flow data are available. The relevant catchment characteristics are extracted from the *Flood Estimation Handbook* CD and are used to calculate the time to peak, T_p, of the unit hydrograph.

AREA	316·27
PROPWET	0·58
BFIHOST	0·411
DPLBAR	20·02
DPSBAR	80·4
SAAR	1273
URBEXT1990	0·06

$$T_p(0) = (4.270 \times DPSBAR^{-0.35}) \times (PROPWET^{-0.80}) \times (DPLBAR^{0.54}(1 + URBEXT)^{-5.77})$$

$T_p(0)$ is found to be 5·12 hours, 20% of this gives a data interval (ΔT) of 1 hour. The time to peak, T_p, is calculated from

$$T_p(\Delta T) = T_p(0) + \frac{\Delta T}{2}$$

$T_p(\Delta T)$ is now referred to as T_p.

The unit hydrograph peak flow and time base are then calculated from T_p, where $U_p = 2.2/T_p \times AREA$

$$TB = 2.52T_p$$

In this case, T_p is 5·6 hours and the unit hydrograph shown in Figure 1.8 is obtained, representing the catchment response to 10 mm of effective rainfall spread uniformly over the catchment.

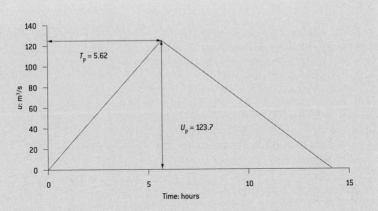

Figure 1.8. Unit hydrograph for the River Kelvin at Killermont

The design storm duration, D, is calculated from

$$D = T_p \left(\frac{1 + SAAR}{1000} \right)$$

Next, the *Flood Estimation Handbook* CD is used to extract the design storm depth, P, for the appropriate rainfall return period. On relative natural catchments (where $URBEXT < 0\cdot125$) the rainfall return period is derived from a graph relating the return period of rainfall events to that of the resulting flood. If the catchment is heavily urbanised, the rainfall and flood return periods are taken to be equal. This design storm depth is termed the T-year D-hour point rainfall ($MT - Dh$) and is scaled using an areal factor to give the catchment rainfall depth.

A catchment wetness index, CWI, and routeing coefficient, RC, are then calculated. CWI is based on the catchment long-term average rainfall and RC is based on the design storm profile. In simple terms, this addresses the extent of urbanisation in the catchment and whether floods will tend to occur in winter (more natural catchments) or summer (urban catchments).

The percentage runoff, *PR*, baseflow, *BF*, and rapid response flood peak, q_t, are then calculated (as detailed in CEHW 1999, Vol. 4). In this case

D = 12 hours
P = 70·77 mm
CWI = 124 mm
RC = 0·425 (based on a 75% winter profile)
PR = 50· 13 mm
BF = 11· 99 m^3s^{-1}
qt = 366·85 m^3s^{-1}

Finally

$$Q_T = q_t + BF$$

The 100–1 chance flood or 1% probability flood for the River Kelvin at Killermont is found to be 378 m^3s^{-1}.

1.6   USE OF COMPUTER MODELS

The current approach to flood estimation in the UK is based on a statistical analysis of existing flood records or an interpretation of the relationship between rainfall and runoff based on catchment characteristics. The accuracy of statistical methods is limited by the quality and availability of historic data. Many gauging stations are calibrated with a bias towards low flows so peak flows can be widely inaccurate, as it is often impossible to access a site at the height of a flood. Other problems are discontinuities in the data caused, for example, by changes in flow regime due to land use changes, climatic trends, or by changes in the location or method of measuring the flow (Section 5.5.4).

Both approaches recommended by the 1975 *Flood Studies Report* and the 1999 *Flood Estimation Handbook* produce estimates of peak flows with associated probabilities, but have been kept separate from the issue of hydraulic modelling of water flow through the catchment. The use of computer models to represent the hydrological cycle began in 1958, when the US Army Corps of Engineers began investigating the use of computer techniques in stream flow analysis and reservoir regulation. From this, several generations of the Stanford Watershed Model were developed, providing a comprehensive conceptual representation of the hydrological cycle, solving equations to describe the catchment processes and a water balance to account for storage within the catchment.

In 1970 a mathematical model adapted from the Stanford Watershed Model was used to simulate the hydrological processes in the Clyde basin in Scotland (Fleming, 1970). Given rainfall, evaporation and catchment data, the model was calibrated for the catchment and then used to produce simulated flows — which were found to be in good agreement with the observed flows. This illustrates that even 30 years ago the technology to use mathematical models to simulate flows was available and, since then, huge advances have been made in the computational modelling of river catchments.

However, computational modelling has not been widely adopted in the UK in the operational field of flood forecasting. The main focus has been on the use of statistical methods (1975 *Flood Studies Report* and 1999 *Flood Estimation Handbook*). There are suitable models available, but they are still not used to anywhere near maximum benefit.

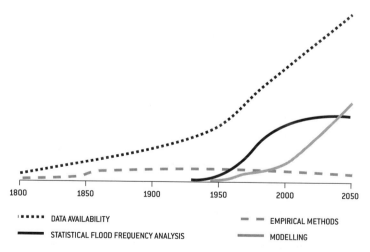

Figure 1.9. How flood data and flood estimation techniques have developed over time

Computer models offer the best means of maximising data utilisation, which is important considering the ever-increasing data collection. Figure 1.9 shows a schematic representation of the different methods used in flood estimation over the last 200 years and a projection of expected developments in the next 50 years. The chart illustrates the huge increase in hydrological and meteorological data available over the last century due to the creation of new gauging stations and the use of radar and satellite imagery.

With increased computing power, increased data, a better understanding of the physical processes, digital terrain maps and more accurate short-term rainfall forecasts, it is now possible to predict flood events with increasing accuracy and in real time. This ability means that computer modelling should become an increasingly important tool within flood risk management.

1.7   HUMAN DIMENSION

When attempting to predict and model, the occurrence and extent of flooding, it is often the case that insufficient weight is being placed by the engineering profession on the human distress caused by flooding — its social impact. The distress is strongly reinforced where flooding is relatively frequent, or where sewage contamination of floodwater has occurred. Studies have occasionally been made of the health and psychiatric impacts of flooding (Bennet, 1970; Flood Hazard Research Centre, 1999). Emotions can still be stirred again many years later, as was seen in a recent television programme on the Lynmouth flood of nearly 50 years ago.

The view from a flood victim

Ros Amor, resident of Barlby, North Yorkshire, whose home was flooded in November 2000

'When my husband and I bought our home we were not aware the property was situated in a flood plain or an area at risk from flooding because of the low-lying levels. We certainly would not have bought the house if these facts were known and available to us. We relied on solicitors acting on our behalf to carry out all appropriate searches prior to signing the contract. They did not reveal anything that gave them cause for concern; indeed, with hindsight, the main focus appeared to have been on the potential for subsidence due to mining rather than the risk of flooding.

'The impact of the floods, in the early hours of 4 November 2000, has left us totally devastated. To be trapped in your home, as were many others, was a terrifying experience. Watching the water surround your home, the noise of garage doors being forced open and being lifted up and taken away, knowing there was nothing to do but watch and wait for it to abate. Hour upon hour we waited with the water getting deeper, in total darkness and extreme cold, with the terrifying noise of things banging into the property as they were swept along by the sheer volume of water. It was like a living nightmare, which will be with me for the rest of my life.

'We were rescued by boat at about 8am, and the relief I felt was unexplainable. As the boat was swept along in the strong current, I looked back at my home totally surrounded by deep, dirty water with our vehicles submerged in the drive, and wondered if I would ever see them again; it was a very eerie feeling.

'Two days later we returned to our home, although the water had abated, it was still very deep outside and I had to be carried to the back door. As I entered, I was unprepared for what greeted me. The stench was sickening; three inches of silt over what used to be my carpets; excrement hanging from the walls; the floors buckled; the fire and surround like a heap of matchwood. In the kitchen the lower units, washing machine, oven and refrigerator were still full of stinking river water and everywhere the brown and orangey silt. Everything was ruined. But this was just the beginning; the heartache of throwing all your possessions, some of which we had all our married life, into a skip and watch them being taken away. It was apparent that it would be many months before the house was habitable again. We had to find temporary accommodation, along with over 300 other families from the

Barlby area alone. Neighbours were scattered near and far countywide. Then another blow, looters began ransacking the properties for what little residents had left. Personal items, which had been taken upstairs out of the path of the floodwater, became targets for thieves and burglars.

'After 10 days we could begin the task of putting our home back together. I certainly had no concept of just what this would entail. First of all everything at ground floor level was wrecked and taken back to an empty shell, then 8–10 weeks to dry out the property before the reinstatement works can begin. New floors, walls, woodwork, doors, kitchen fittings, sanitary ware, total re-wiring of the electrical system, central heating and plumbing. There was no normality or stability to our lives; you simply live from day to day not knowing what will happen next. Crisis followed crisis; there were times when I didn't want to return to my home, it hurt so much. My husband had to devote all his energies to getting our home back together and his business, built up over many years, had to take second place. It will take a long time to recover.

'Since returning home in April 2001, I have reflected many times on the events leading up to the flood. The warnings we received were "precautionary" which does not mean life threatening. At no time were we told of the impending dangers as they became apparent. The information residents received was totally inadequate and confusing to the say the least. There are many lessons to be learned — not just Barlby, but other parts of the country who were affected in the same way

- flood warnings need to be made available to everyone who could be affected at the earliest possible time; it is important to be able to move some of your personal possessions to safety — it really can make a difference
- accurate information is very important; people need to know what is going on; in the case of Barlby, local residents could see for themselves the state of the river several days before the breach, but calls to the local council were ignored or fobbed off — "it will not happen"

- help, advice and support systems need to be better organised following a flood — it was obvious that our local council had no proper strategy or contingency plan in place — not just for flooding but any kind of emergency.

'Since January 2001, I have been attending the Flood Defence Committee meetings, as an interested member of the public, and will continue to do so. Attendance at these meetings has certainly opened by eyes to the manner in which decisions, which potentially affect thousands of homes in the area, are made. The voting members appear to be more concerned with keeping their position in whichever local authority they represent than in what needs to be done — unless it affects their particular patch. I have watched officers of the Environment Agency pleading for additional levy in order to make a start at resolving the problems that years of neglect and lack of maintenance have caused, not just in Barlby, but Stamford Bridge, Malton, Norton and Gowdall, to name a few in Yorkshire. This will be replicated throughout the country. Central government must instigate a thorough overhaul of the entire system for funding flood defence work. The main points, from my perspective are

1. reports on the state of flood defences need to be acted upon – not just filed away; prevention is better than a very expensive flood
2. flood defence decisions need to be made on professional judgements, not political interference
3. this is a national problem, not just Barlby
4. flood defence is about people and people's lives; surely it is more cost effective to be pro-active than re-active.'

2 *Flood risk*

Stephen Huntingdon and Kenneth MacDougall

2.1 ASSESSING RISK

2.1.1 *Existing approaches*

Floods are a natural occurrence and the risk they pose is wide ranging. However, in societal terms, the main focus is the risk to people and property. It is neither practically nor economically feasible to eliminate all flood risk. The most suitable approach for dealing with flooding must therefore be to manage the risk best.

To date the technical approach for designing protection has been to focus on the certainty of flood defences to give confidence. There are methodologies available to engineers that can allow relatively accurate predictions of where flooding will occur and, given a particular magnitude of flood, the extent of flooding, duration, rate of rise, flood depths, velocities and damage can all be predicted. Regrettably these techniques have not been applied sufficiently widely. The main uncertainty in flooding is the timing of when it will occur, as lead times may frequently be only in the order of hours.

The traditional design approach focuses on the design flood event, typically the 1% annual probability of flooding. Providing the flood alleviation measure is appropriate for the predicted magnitude of flood, including a suitable freeboard margin for bank settlement, wave allowance, modelling inaccuracies and other uncertainties, it is assumed that protection has been achieved for the relevant design period. A degree of risk is therefore accounted for within the design, however, it may often not be explicit, and it does not take account of the impact of floods greater than the design event.

2.1.2 Dynamic conditions and uncertainty

It is important to recognise that because both the baseline and flood event conditions are dynamic, the flood risk is also dynamic. This means that variations and uncertainties will occur and must be accounted for. This is true both during an actual flood event (e.g. 12 hours) and over the design life to protect against flood events (e.g. 60 years). The traditional approach does not specifically address uncertainty within the design process. There is a wide range of factors that can give rise to uncertainties, from environmental loading to the structural performance of defences. Unless these uncertainties are identified and addressed, designs will be vulnerable. Risk-based approaches are well suited to dealing with uncertainties, and can provide the best available means for guiding the design.

2.1.3 Understanding real risk

The dynamic conditions mentioned also arise from factors such as increasing pressures on development, limited resources, climate change and increasing sophistication of society. The result is a need to address and convey the real situation of risk and increase awareness. Flood awareness will ultimately depend on the experience of individuals, both in terms of design engineers and people affected. This first-hand experience will reinforce the consequences of flooding, and raise awareness. Lack of flood awareness can be problematic, especially in areas where the population has not experienced flooding, either due to lack of recent flood events, or high population turnovers. Figure 2.1 illustrates how various factors affect the tolerance of risk, both on an individual and societal scale.
Risk communication is of major importance. People generally have higher risk tolerances when they are aware of the issues and can make an informed judgement themselves. To manage the risk successfully, we must clearly understand what constitutes a flood risk, and how this will vary depending on individual and collective perspectives.

2.1.4 Wider benefits of risk approach

A comprehensive flood risk assessment encompasses economic, social and environmental issues, as well as the technical aspects and uncertainties of flood magnitude and damage (Figure 2.2). However,

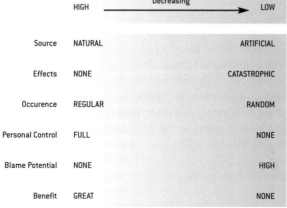

Figure 2.1. Risk tolerance matrix (MacDougall, 1999)

Figure 2.2. Factors affecting flood risk include economic, social and environmental issues

in the context of this report, the technical aspect is the main focus. A risk-based approach clearly identifies various components of the problem and associated consequences, and this key feature enables valid comparisons to be made with other investment decisions to protect and support society.

There is a clear need to increase routine use of risk-based techniques by all professionals involved. The technology is available but is not fully applied at present. Risk-based assessments will encourage a more comprehensive investigation of uncertainties and identify where more information is required, allowing more focused practical research to be undertaken.

2.2 DEFINING RISK

The flood risk or the exposure to flood hazard must be clearly understood and communicated to all concerned. To ensure this, it is important that appropriate and consistent terminology is used.

Hazard

A situation with the *potential* to result in harm. A hazard does not necessarily lead to harm.

Pathway

Provides the connection between a particular hazard being realised and the receptor that may be harmed. For example, the *pathway* may consist of the flood defences and flood plain between a flow in the river channel (the *source*) and a housing development (the *receptor*).

Receptor

Receptor refers to the asset that may be harmed. For example, in the event of heavy rainfall (the *source*) flood water may propagate across the flood plain (the *pathway*) and inundate housing (the *receptor*) that may suffer material damage (the *harm* or *consequence*)

Residual risk
The risk which remains after risk management and mitigation. May include, for example, damage predicted to continue to occur during storm events of greater severity than the 1 year return period.

Risk
Combination of probability and consequence.

Risk assessment
Consideration of hazards inherent in a project and the risks associated with them.

Risk management
The activity of mitigating and monitoring risks, which predominantly occurs after the project appraisal stage.

Source
Source is synonymous with hazard and refers to a situation with the potential for harm (for example, heavy rainfall, strong winds, surge, etc.).

Tolerability
Tolerability does not mean acceptability. It refers to willingness to live with a risk to secure certain benefits and in the confidence that it is being properly controlled. To tolerate a risk means that we do not regard it as negligible, or something we might ignore, but rather as something we need to keep under review, and reduce still further if and as we can.

Vulnerability
Refers to the resilience of a particular demographic group, animal or bird to respond to a hazardous condition. For example, elderly people may be less able to evacuate in the event of a rapid flood than young people.

The source–pathway–receptor model is a useful method of establishing risk relationships. In relation to flooding, it can easily be seen that management of the risk is heavily biased to the receptor end of the scale (Figure 2.3). The source (precipitation) cannot be controlled and, whereas the pathway (land and watercourses) can have scope for management, ultimately the receptor (people and property) can be controlled the most.

One of the key aims of flood risk assessment is to understand and be aware of the complexities of the situation as best as possible, then to simplify the situation down to an acceptable level to allow practical measures to be put in place. When the risk of a particular event is expressed, the perception of risk can vary, both in scope and scale. Thus, it is important to define at the outset what is the context of the risk and how it relates to hazard.

We must be aware that risk is dynamic both in time and space, and the risk assessment must reflect this. A static system cannot be assumed and continual review is essential, every five to ten years or subsequent to any major changes in the catchment. Figure 2.4 illustrates how future risks may vary along with some of the processes that may influence how the nature and magnitude of the risk can change in the future.

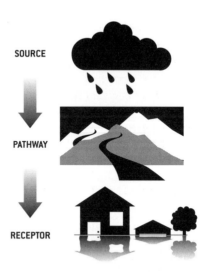

Figure 2.3. Source–pathway–receptor model for floods — we have the greatest control over the receptor

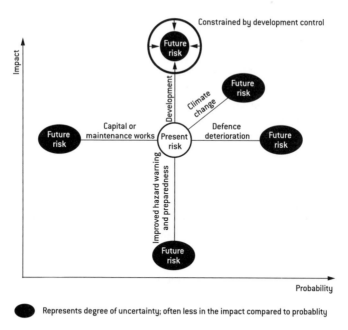

Figure 2.4. The dynamics of risk (HR Wallingford, 2001)

Risk-based approaches will tend to provide more information than is available from deterministic analysis. They will often lead to the possibility of a wide range of potential solutions with differing costs and benefits. This information must be provided in as concise and clear a format as possible. This is especially true where uncertainties are concerned, where they should be identified as being inherent or theoretical, and appropriate confidence levels assigned.

2.3   HOLISTIC APPROACH TO FLOOD RISK MANAGEMENT

Within river systems, flooding is the natural way for the system to discharge the water arising from the occasional large rainfall event. There is no problem at all until man decides to use some of the natural flood plain for his own use, and chooses to protect against inundation. We then face the dilemma of protecting against a natural hazard for the benefit of mankind that has chosen to live and work in flood plain areas. To many, the defence against flooding is the construction of engineering structures, such as walls and barriers, to prevent floodwaters inundating those areas we have chosen to develop. However attractive this may appear, total application of this solution with limited resources is impractical, uneconomic and unsustainable.

We do not have defences in all places where flooding may occur, those defences we have are built to varying standards (in some areas, such as London, the defence standard is much higher), and some defences are structurally weak and cannot deliver the level of service for which they were initially constructed. Even where we have a defence structure performing to design specification, it is accepted that the level of protection may be exceeded on extreme occasions — but not so extreme to be beyond reasonable expectation. Indeed, by designing our defences so that they do not overtop for the 1% annual probability of flooding, we are accepting that for those severe events with a probability less than 1% in any year, overtopping may occur.

Hence, inundation following severe rainfall events must be regarded as a realistic possibility in some places at some times. However, the uncertainty of the where and when compound our difficulty.

It is of paramount importance that this level of uncertainty is carefully communicated to the public at risk, to raise general awareness of the vulnerability to potential flooding and to develop an understanding of the situation without causing unnecessary alarm. The discussion of the failure of an engineered system to perform is not a commonly occurring need, and we have perhaps been reluctant to discuss these issues sufficiently widely. This dilemma is also occurring in the Netherlands at present, where the population has a faith in their river embankments, which is regarded by experts as too confident. The creation of awareness of the consequences and actions to be taken if failure occurs is being raised on the flood management agenda in that country.

Recognition of the risk of failure, reinforces the argument for the holistic approach to flood risk management. This approach does not trust absolutely in the ability of engineered flood alleviation measures to prevent flooding. Recognising that flooding will occur in some instances, we need to supplement our flood alleviation measures with flood response measures.

Flood response activities will include preparations, such as

- installation of foundations for demountable flood defences

- making buildings more resistant to flood damage
- development of a reliable flood warning system
- planning of appropriate emergency response.

Flood response at the time of flooding will involve

- use of the flood warning system
- implementation of temporary flood defences
- measures to protect valuables
- mobilisation of emergency services.

After the flooding event, the flood response activities will involve the whole gamut of necessary recovery actions that, it is hoped, will enhance the preparedness and resistance to damage of subsequent

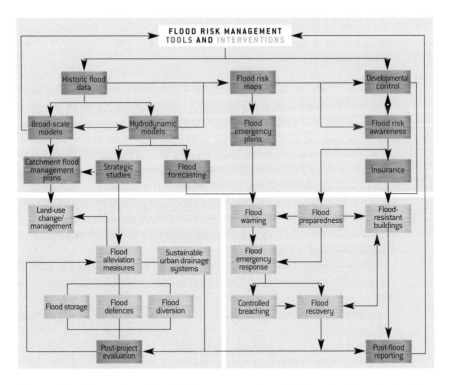

Figure 2.5. The matrix of flood risk management needs to be clearly understood

floods. And, to be able to do the necessary design and development of systems to enable us to put alleviation and response measures in place, we need an understanding of the processes contributing to the flooding (Figure 2.5).

For all response measures it is important that professionals develop their plans and then communicate them to the public at risk. Members of the public need to be fully informed of their vulnerability and aware of the procedures that will be implemented during times of high flood risk. To achieve this we need to communicate and inform on a continuous basis, requiring imaginative and varied modes of communication from use of the media to local flood information fairs. If this is done properly we can hope to mobilise the cooperation of a prepared and responsive public in the process of flood risk management. In this way we should be able to minimise the total damage arising from flooding.

2.4 COMMUNICATING RISK

2.4.1 Flood awareness

Prior to 1998, the UK had experienced 30 years without flooding of sufficient significance to capture the attention of the population at large. There were, of course, many instances of flooding in the UK in that period, both coastal and fluvial, which were of dramatic significance to those involved but they were geographically local in their impact. There was also an awareness of widespread flooding catastrophes in other parts of the world.

But it has been the flooding of 1998 and 2000 that has awoken the whole of England and Wales to the realisation that flooding is a natural hazard which, on occasions, may be of widespread national significance (Figures 2.6–2.8). Predictions of the consequences of climate change exacerbating such events have captured the public imagination. There is now a public expectation that flood risk will be better managed and resourced in the future.

The public awakening is not at all surprising. Research undertaken (RIBAMOD, 1999; EUROTAS, 1998) has identified a widely occurring cycle of flooding, investment and complacency until the next flooding event (Figure 2.9). It is easy to imagine the difficulties confronting funders and flood management professionals to maintain flood management funding and alertness throughout a period longer

Figure 2.6. Flood preparedness and awareness applies equally to transport infrastructure in flood risk areas. In this example the railway station appears to more resemble a canal during the flood event

Figure 2.7. In the aftermath of flood events the process of recovery begins. This recovery time and effort must be included as an integral part of the flood risk assessment process

Figure 2.8. Lack of flood awareness and preparedness can lead to people being stranded in their own homes

than a generation when other pressures on the public purse are relentlessly present, year upon year. In periods of sensitivity to the importance of, and widespread potential for, flooding events, it is crucial that full advantage is taken to communicate some of the key aspects of local flood risk management as it is being developed. It is also important to ensure that we manage the expectations of people at

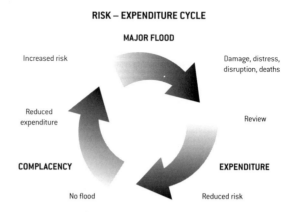

Figure 2.9. Risk-expenditure cycle shows how complacency increases flood risk

risk from flooding, to ensure that it is understood that we cannot prevent flooding — we can only strive to reduce its adverse impacts.

2.4.2 Locations at risk

The first issue we have to communicate is the vulnerability of any location to flooding. For those areas that do not flood on a regular basis this information has been very sparse and not well documented. However, recent initiatives by the Environment Agency to place flood risk outlines on CD and the internet have made this information available to all. Nevertheless, the internet is not used by all; neither will all wish to use it as a source of information. Continuous awareness can be achieved in other ways.

In Germany, in areas vulnerable to flooding along the Rhine, rings are painted around lamp posts to indicate previous flood levels or predicted flood levels for a certain probability of occurrence. Central London had a similar approach for the high-risk years before the Thames Barrier gave it substantial protection against a tidal surge. This technique reminds all local residents of the ever-present threat and offers a secure way of ensuring that newcomers are made aware of the potential risk very shortly after moving to the vicinity. The Bye Report, published by the Environment Agency to draw lessons from the Easter 1998 floods in central England, lent its weight to the publicity value of such a marking of the expected flood surface for the 1% annual probability of flooding (Environment Agency, 1998). The marking of historic flood levels in prominent places in the urban environment is a very simple means of keeping people aware and informed. The marks will be revised with the passage of time, showing successive floods and thereby keeping the memory of events alive, as well as giving information of relative severity.

2.4.3 Expressing the risk

The most difficult concept to convey is that of the risk of flood events occurring. We have expressed the extreme nature of the event by taking the average period between events as 'The Return Period'. However, by trying to make the understanding of probability more straightforward, we have introduced an idea of periodicity — but this has begun to mislead the non-expert. For example, the design exceedance of the majority of fluvial flood defences has been set at a probability of 1% in any year. This event has been translated into having a return period of 100 years. After any large event deemed to have a return period of 100 years or more, many will regard it, perhaps complacently, as most unlikely such an event will reoccur in their lifetime. However, the same probability applies for any year, including the one immediately after a large event.

The difference between odds and probabilities should be noted. If the odds on a horse are 3 to 1, this translates to a 1 in 4 chance or 25% probability that the horse will win the race, or a 3 in 4 or 75% probability that the horse will not finish first. For higher odds or more unlikely events, such as the 100 to 1 flood, technically there is a 1 in 101 chance that a flood event will occur in a given year, however this rounds to a 1% probability and is generally quoted as such (Jones, 2001).

Taking the 1% probability over a reasonably long time period of a lifetime of 70 years, it can be shown that what is today referred to as a 1-in-100 year flood has a 50% chance of occurrence within the 70-year lifetime period. More significantly, a 1-in-100 year flood has a 15% chance of occurring twice in that lifetime (Figure 2.10).

By conveying probability without a time period, it becomes obvious that the broader issues of continuous communication to maintain awareness are essential.

The understanding of odds is widespread, arising in many sports involving gambling. Therefore, in communicating flood risk to the general public, instead of referring to the '100-year flood', this could

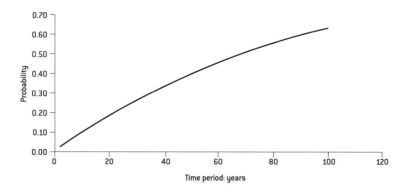

Figure 2.10. Probability graph for 100-1 flood

be approximated to 'a 100–1 chance against the flood in question being equalled or exceeded in any year', in other words a '100–1 chance flood'. Other things being equal, the odds would remain the same each year, regardless of any recent severe occurrences.

For communicating risk to professionals, the alternative terminology of '1% annual probability of flooding' can also be used. However, the use of the concept of return period should be discouraged in all communication.

2.5   BEST PRACTICE FOR UK FLOOD RISK MANAGEMENT

2.5.1   Need in the decision-making process

The resources for the implementation of our flood risk management infrastructure and procedures will be funded largely through the public purse — partially central funding and partially local — augmented by developers' contributions. It is essential that a reliable and systematic way of prioritising financial support is developed, taking into account the uncertainties inherent in the occurrence of flooding.

A strategic and holistic approach to this challenge is contained within the *Flood and Coastal Defence Project Appraisal Guidance* issued by the Department for Environment, Food and Rural Affairs (DEFRA) in 1999 (MAFF, 1999a) and currently used for scheme selection. This covers

- economic justification
- need to embrace probabilistic techniques
- inclusion of environmental damage mitigation and enhancement.

The series of guidance documents is recognised as being an advanced approach to decision-making in an environment of scarce resource. The guides are based on straightforward strategic principles, yet allow deviation from the simple underlying approach for those cases justifying a different approach due to particular reasons.

Within every stage of the decision-making process, ranging from financial appraisal through to engineering performance, there are many uncertainties. Within a risk-based framework, it is important that all sources of uncertainty are at least identified and, if possible, quantified within the overall decision-making process. Figure 2.11 illustrates some examples where uncertainties are categorised generically under the two general headings of natural variability and knowledge uncertainty.

There are various methods available to introduce and assess risk within the decision-making process. Two methods of conceptualising the risk are

- *Risk Decision Box* — this can be used to provide an assessment of risk based on two parameters relating to likelihood of occurrence and the magnitude of the consequences (Figure 2.12)
- *Risk Bubble* — this method plots various risk indicators on different axes, allowing a greater number of parameters to be assessed, and the comparative performances of different options can be assessed (Figure 2.13).

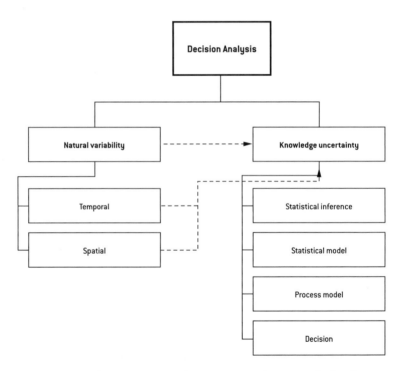

Figure 2.11. Generic sources of uncertainty inherent with the decision process (HR Wallingford, 2001)

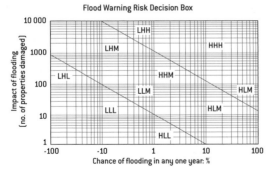

Category	Probability	Impact	Risk
HHH	High	High	High
HLH	High	Low	High
LHH	Low	High	High
HHM	High	High	Medium
HLM	High	Low	Medium
LHM	Low	High	Medium
LLM	Low	Low	Medium
HLL	High	Low	Low
LHL	Low	High	Low
LLL	Low	Low	Low

Probability: The danger of a given flood occuring in one year
Impact: The number of properties liable to be flooded by a given flood
Risk: The weighted combination of probability and impact

Structure of flood warning system/awareness programme:

Category/Risk	Awareness Programme Intensity	Direct Warnings	Indirect Warnings	Major Incident Plans
HHH/High	High	Selected	Yes	Yes
HLH/High	High	Yes	Yes	No
LHH/High	High	Selected	Yes	Yes
HHM/Medium	High	Selected	Yes	Yes
HLM/Medium	High	Yes	Yes	No
LHM/Medium	Medium	Selected	Yes	Yes
LLM/Medium	Medium	Selected	Yes	No
HLL/Low	High	Yes	Yes	No
LHL/Low	Low	No	Yes	Yes
LLL/Low	Low	No	Yes	No

Figure 2.12. Environment Agency flood forecasting risk decision box (HR Wallingford, 2001)

Both of the above methods can be used to determine zones of acceptable, tolerable and unacceptable risks.

2.5.2 Consistency

At first sight it might appear logical to seek consistency by choosing a common standard of defence for all flood alleviation measures. However, this approach would mean that defences would be built without regard to the value of the assets protected.

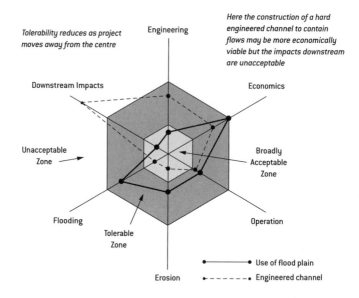

Figure 2.13. Example of acceptable risk bubble for fluvial flood defence

At the other extreme, funding could be allocated to defences based on a strict cost-benefit analysis. In this situation the consistency appears not in the standard of defence, but in the process leading to the decision whether to build a defence in one location or another. This approach also offers a logical way of prioritisation, so that the most valuable schemes are given the highest priority.

Taking the cost-benefit approach to its logical conclusion, we would find that areas of lesser asset value would receive defences of a lower level of protection. This approach is perfectly logical in economic terms, but is it acceptable in societal terms?

The present DEFRA appraisal guidance generally follows the latter route of consistency of approach rather than consistency of standard. However, it also aims to set a range of standards of defence in most situations.

Should people be prepared to abandon their houses if they are built on flood plains to allow rivers to flood?

Extracted from 'Debate: Homes built on flood plains', published in *New Civil Engineer*, 22 November 2001

YES

Flood plains are part of the natural river system, providing a capacity for flood waters to flow unimpeded and storage to reduce peak flow downstream. Past development has restricted the beneficial function of flood plains and increased levels of flood risk to those living in other areas. In addition to changes brought about by flood plain development, climate change scenarios predict that peak flows for a given return period could increase by up to 20% in 50 years.

Flood defence policy-makers and planners have to take a catchment wide view of sustainable flood risk management and protect the public in general. The best option to reduce flood risk in some urban communities is to remove critical buildings and widen the river corridor to increase flow capacity, as is often done abroad. This may involve the acquisition of, with appropriate compensation, property on land needed for flood storage. Flood defence can only be provided when it is cost effective, however people in isolated unprotected houses within the flood plain must be given assistance in adapting to increased flood risk and in making their properties more flood resistant.

The Environment Agency is championing the use of local flood protection and flood resistant construction however it must be accepted that there will be extreme cases where increased flooding and the cost of maintaining the fabric will lead to other houses being abandoned.

(Based on published text by Dr Mervyn Bramley, Flood Defence Development Manager.)

NO

Historically, Bewdley has been subject to regular flooding and people are generally aware of this when they purchase property and accept the associated risk of intermittent flooding. Over a period of time the community builds up local flooding knowledge, puts a support network in place and householders take steps to make their homes more flood resistant. However, after a major flood event property prices drop, insurance companies withdraw flood cover and mortgages become increasingly difficult to obtain. After events such as these it is important that insurance money for flood damage repair is spent with a view to increasing flood resistance for the next event.

In Bewdley, after the floods of 2000, the Environment Agency is developing a scheme to protect around 150 houses from flooding while maintaining the character of the river front. However, a further 32 properties will remain unprotected as they do not meet the cost-benefit analysis criteria for the funding. While defence would be welcome in this area, residents feel that with sufficient warning, upper floors to store possessions and the knowledge that flooding is likely, then it is possible to live with a level of intermittent flooding.

Listed buildings in conservation areas, such as Bewdley, should be protected from flooding to protect our heritage. However, newer houses built in flood plain developments are often bought by people unaware of the associated flood risk, and these people should either be provided with an acceptable level of flood protection or provided with compensation to move.

(Based on published text by Gillian Holland, Secretary, Bewdley Residents Flood Defence Committee.)

2.5.3 Cost-benefit evaluation

It is important that the health and social benefits are incorporated as fully as possible within the cost-benefit justification of the scheme. It can be argued that inclusion of costs for health and social benefits would give a higher and more realistic benefit-cost ratio. In the short term, this does not give an improvement on the total investment or number of schemes, as the overall rate of scheme development depends on the limited spend within the allocated resource. However, in the longer term, a more realistic appraisal of true benefit will allow a comparison of the benefits of flood defence expenditure compared to other Treasury-dependent investment opportunities.

Of more value in the short term is the ability to improve the prioritisation of potential schemes by reducing some of the perceived shortcomings of the present system. For example, a benefit-cost analysis may give greater priority to a scheme protecting an area with a low housing density in south-east England than a scheme of high density housing in north-east England, solely due to differences in property values. Were health and social costs included, the balance would be weighted more toward the scheme of high density but lower property value. Similarly, schemes involving housing would be advanced compared to those involving industrial premises due to the inclusion of greater people-related benefits.

The practical difficulties preventing change in the short term are the lack of monetary values that can be attributed to many health and social benefits. Some progress is being made with the monetary evaluation of environmental benefits, but little data exists for avoidance of social distress. The small amount of research carried out indicates that these intangible impacts may be of similar magnitude to the tangible or direct impacts for areas of housing. However, it must be pointed out that the DEFRA appraisal approach already recognises the importance of these factors, even though it is recognised that monetary values are not readily available. Recommendation is given to include monetary impacts wherever possible, and suggestions of analogies that can be made to determine such impacts are given. Ultimately, though, it is recognised that there may be remaining non-monetary impacts that should be considered and presented as part of the argument for the investment decision.

Fortunately, fatalities directly attributable to flooding in the UK are sufficiently rare that they do not routinely figure in such appraisals. The last major flood causing many fatalities was the east coast flood of 1953, when 300 lives were lost. It is likely that if that tidal surge event were to be repeated with the present level of flood warning and raised defences, the number of fatalities would be significantly reduced. Over the last few decades fatalities directly due to flooding have been about one per year, far less than fatality rates for any mode of transport. However, if a particular situation arises where potential fatalities are a realistic issue, the DEFRA appraisal guidance notes require specific mention of this fact as a non-monetary impact, as above.

2.5.4 Standards of defence

Indicative standards of defence have been given in the DEFRA appraisal guidance for each of several land uses. These standards are provided to the promoter of a scheme to target an appropriate range of options.

However, it is generally accepted that we may be in a period of more rapid climate change than previously (see Chapter 7) and that schemes giving a certain protection today may offer less protection for the same probability of flood event in the future. Although we cannot be certain about increased flood flows in the future, it is recommend that scheme design should extend the analysis to look at sensitivity to flows higher than the present design flow to take into account climatic and land use changes.

In any case, extending the impact analysis to events more severe than the design event is good practice in helping identify vulnerability of high value or strategic facilities, and also to contribute to the emergency planning process. It may also result in the identification of the need for secondary defences for those strategic facilities.

2.5.5 Standards of preparedness and response

At present there appears to be a disconnection between the provision of flood alleviation measures and all the other aspects of holistic flood risk management that are brought to bear when the flood alleviation measures are inadequate for the magnitude of event. There seems to be no overall risk assessment of the whole process, nor setting of target standards for response activities.

The previous sections have noted the strategic framework available to assist the decision making for investment in capital works in a complex situation riddled with uncertainty. This same rigour should be applied to investment decisions associated with flood preparedness and flood response measures. It is likely that the same principles will apply, so progress can be made without rewriting any guidance.

Types of British river flooding

Sudden onset in natural catchments
where telemetered information is unlikely to be effective in allowing damage avoidance, but may prevent loss of life.

- Catastrophic local rainstorm, typically 125+ mm rain in a few hours at centre (Lynmouth August 1952, Louth May 1920, Bristol July 1968).
- Breach of flood levee (Over, Cambridgeshire Fens, March 1947).
- Dam-break (or canal-bank-breach) flood.
- 'Sunny-day' flood, due to geotechnical or structural failure.
- Storm overtopping.
- Ice-jam flood (Medway, January 1814).

Seasonal saturation flooding in natural catchments
where catchment telemetry can be expected to lead to damage avoidance.

- Regional flooding (Autumn 2000, Easter 1998, December 1979, September 1968).
- Groundwater flooding (Chichester 1993, Chilterns/South Downs 2001).
- Snowmelt, often triggered by rain (north-east England especially, January 1982; widespread, March 1947).
- Rain on snow on frozen ground (January 1809 on upper Thames/Bristol Avon).
- River flood, high tide and sea surge into estuary coincide (Gainsborough).
- Landslide blocking flow before washing out.
- 'Bog-burst' (Solway Moss 1771, Tees headwaters 1934).
- Rising-bed flood, due to aggradation or cessation of dredging.

3 Catchment and river basin management

Lindsay Frost and Donald Knight

3.1 STRATEGIC RIVER BASIN MANAGEMENT

3.1.1 Need for a strategic approach

Traditionally, flood defences were provided as individual local schemes with little consideration as to their impact across the wider river catchment. This approach has been changing over recent years. It now seems self-evident that individual flood alleviation schemes cannot be considered in isolation and that what happens in one part of the catchment will have effects on other areas some distance away. Accordingly, there is now almost universal agreement that a more strategic, catchment-based approach to flood risk management is warranted.

The move to a more strategic catchment-based, approach does not simply mean a wider view on investment in flood defences. It means taking a holistic view of flood risk management, including built development and land management patterns, nature conservation constraints and opportunities, and emergency planning arrangements. This needs to be based on a long-term view up to 50 years ahead, backed by sophisticated modelling of the dynamic physical processes at work in the catchment. All this will drive a major change to the way in which flood risk is managed in England and Wales.

3.1.2 Catchment flood management planning in England and Wales

The move to strategic, integrated, catchment management has been accelerating in recent years. This has been driven by

- research literature and evolving good practice
- comparisons with practice in other countries
- experience of serious flood events, such as Easter 1998
- impending European Union legislation.

As far back as 1993, the Ministry for Agriculture, Fisheries and Food's (MAFF) *Strategy for Flood and Coast Defence* (MAFF, 1993) advocated a strategic catchment-wide approach to flood defence. This was reiterated in 1997 (MAFF, 1997). However, there appears to have been no clear national commitment to the preparation of river catchment plans, in contrast to the progress made during the 1990s on shoreline management plans along the coast. A specific target for promotion of a strategic approach to fluvial flood risk was not included in the *High Level Targets for Flood and Coastal Defence* published in November 1999 (MAFF, 1999b).

MAFF developed the idea of a national programme to prepare catchment flood management plans. In February 2000, the Welsh Assembly introduced a requirement for such plans into its draft *High Level Targets for Wales*. A programme of work to the same end is now being advanced in England by DEFRA and the Environment Agency. Over the next five years, it is anticipated that some 60–80 plans will be required to cover the whole of England and Wales, based on catchments of between 1000 and 5000 km². The work of preparing the plans will be led by the Environment Agency and will utilise up to £6 million of extra funding from DEFRA to speed up the process.

Draft interim guidelines on the preparation of catchment flood management plans are currently the subject of consultation with interested parties (Halcrow Water, 2001). In parallel, five pilot studies are being carried out to test and develop the methodology in the following catchments

- Yorkshire Derwent
- Irwell
- Upper Severn
- Medway
- Somerset Levels and Moors (Parrett).

It is hoped that feedback from consultation, together with the completion of the pilot studies will allow publication of formal guidance for preparing catchment plans in early 2002. The main

Good practice in flood risk management: case study A

Gainsborough, Lincolnshire: provision of flood defences as a catalyst for regeneration

Gainsborough is a historic market town on the east bank of the tidal River Trent. The town has a long history as a river port. However, over the last three decades, the port and associated river-based industries have suffered serious decline, leading to dereliction in the town's riverside areas.

The town is vulnerable to river flooding, which can be exacerbated by tidal surges. Gainsborough's flood defences were in poor condition, often being founded on structures more than a century old.

Local authority plans for economic regeneration of the riverside, and the need to upgrade the flood defences, had an obvious overlap. The two were brought together in the Gainsborough Regeneration Partnership, a broadly based group, which successfully bid for £3.6 million of Single Regeneration Budget (SRB) funding.

The flood defence works began in February 1996 and were completed in November 2000 (Figure 3.1). Some 800 m of new flood defences were constructed, protecting the town against a 200–1 chance flood each year. The scheme utilises the Beckingham Marshes, on the Nottinghamshire bank opposite the town, as a natural flood storage area adding to Gainsborough's defences. Overall the flood defence works cost £16 million, providing protection to 400 properties.

The wider programme of regeneration has included

- provision of a new riverside walkway
- a high quality environment for new residential and commercial development
- an innovative riverside Public Arts Trail
- development of Gainsborough's potential as a tourist destination.

Figure 3.1. Flood defences at Gainsborough were built as part of the town's regeneration

The project is likely to be a catalyst for the further regeneration of Gainsborough for several years to come as the local community and commercial developers respond to the opportunities it has created.

Further information:

* www.gainsboroughriverside.org.uk

programme of plan preparation will then follow, with priority catchments identified through initial scoping studies. It is intended that all the scoping studies, and full plans for priority catchments, will be prepared by 2003. The plans will require regular review, particularly if the catchment is subject to significant change through, for example, increased development pressure or changes in farming practices or from suffering a serious flood event.

Caravan parks in Shakespeare country

After the crisis evacuations along the Warwickshire Avon flood plain at the height of the Easter 1998 flood, the Environment Agency asked Cheltenham and Gloucester College of Education Geography Department (soon to be the University of Gloucestershire) to review the risks posed by almost 30 caravan parks along the edge of this river, all within easy reach of Stratford.

One lesson learned followed from the geomorphology of many lowland flood plains, which have a back-ditch that helps drain the land after temporary flooding. Vehicle access to flood plain caravan sites is often over a low unobtrusive bridge across this ditch. When a rare flood occurs, the depth of flow across this dip at the back of the flood plain becomes too great for normal emergency vehicles to cross. Having to resort to boats and helicopters to remove residents then becomes much more complex and expensive. Nor can those who are slow to leave in their own cars get out safely.

Floods can often occur at night and during weekends when families have arrived for a short break with all their belongings, and they are reluctant to follow the first flood warnings because of the disruption it causes to long laid plans.

At the other end of the spectrum, it was found that, for some, the caravan park was their only home in England. Winter would be spent by retirees in the warmth of Spain or Portugal, returning to low-cost caravan life in England for the rest of the year. During the Easter 1998 flood there were several people who had nowhere else to which they could move quickly, even though the caravan park at the time of planning approval had only been visualised as holiday accommodation.

Additional problems of these sites are better known, such as the floatability of caravans and the likelihood of them not being anchored. They can also flip in a strong associated windstorm (or possibly in a rescue helicopter downdraught). Inevitably, such sites, once authorised , grow and 'creep' towards the river view, which makes them attractive, without properly counting the cost of the flood risk that exists. Their temporary residents are not likely to know local flood warning procedures.

The preparation of catchment plans needs to be seen in the wider context of the EU's Water Framework Directive (European Union, 2000), which came into force in December 2000. The Directive requires EU countries to introduce integrated, sustainable, river basin management as successive elements of the Directive are introduced over the next 20 years. It goes beyond catchment plans in seeking holistic management of the water cycle, embracing matters such as water supply and pollution control. In due course, catchment flood management plans will need to be more fully integrated with the requirements of the Water Framework Directive.

Good practice in flood risk management: case study B

Wakefield, West Yorkshire: use of sustainability assessment in preparing flood alleviation schemes

The City of Wakefield has long suffered from flooding by the River Calder. The existing flood defences have been provided in a piecemeal manner over the years. In places, they are approaching the end of their design life and generally are considered inadequate in the event of a 100–1 chance flood. The Environment Agency's flood alleviation scheme combines upstream flood storage, in the form of a controlled 'washland' system, and new and raised flood defences through the city.

The concept of sustainable development is increasingly evident in the preparation and appraisal of flood defence schemes, as commended in DEFRA's project appraisal guidance notes and the UK strategy for sustainable construction. However, there remains a need for a simple, transferable, methodology to guide and promote sustainable schemes at the strategic and project level.

This gap has been met by a methodology called SPeAR™ developed by the scheme's consultant engineers. The method identifies a wide range of sustainability indicators (social, economic, environmental and use of natural resources) for flood defence schemes. This allows positive and negative aspects of schemes to be evaluated, then adapted and improved to reduce adverse impacts and increase social, economic and environmental benefits.

This method can be used iteratively from outline design stage through to detailed design and implementation. It can also be weighted to reflect local priorities, as revealed by consultation with the local community.

In the Wakefield case, application of the method resulted in a number of scheme enhancements and some significant cost savings. The method continues to be used as each phase of the scheme is implemented towards final completion in September 2002.

Further information:

- www.nefas.co.uk/wakefield

3.1.3   Scope of catchment flood management plans

Catchment flood management plans aim to identify long-term, sustainable, policies to assist in the management of flood risk throughout a catchment. They should deliver an integrated package of strategic flood management policies. The whole exercise is underpinned by broad-scale modelling based on a sound understanding of the physical processes at work in the catchment which influence the generation, spread and frequency of flooding. Modelling will allow not only the testing of flood scenarios based on current catchment conditions, but also a dynamic perspective through investigation of future scenarios with various climate change and development assumptions.

It is currently envisaged that each catchment flood management plan will be a fairly high-level document, subdividing the river basin into a series of sub-catchments in which different (but integrated) strategies for flood risk management might be pursued. The nature of these broad strategies has not yet been developed in the pilot studies. However, one possible outcome is a strategic division between 'natural' and 'managed' areas, reflecting mainly rural and urban sub-catchments respectively.

The interim guidelines suggest that the strategic policies in each catchment plan will need to be elaborated at two lower levels. First, strategy plans for sub-catchments will be required to identify appropriate types of policy to deliver catchment plan objectives in that part of the catchment, taking account of social, economic and environmental considerations. Second, following approval of the strategy plan, specific schemes are worked up in option form, and then compared and evaluated prior to detailed design and funding applications. An extract from the draft interim guidelines illustrates the relationship of the three stages (Figure 3.2).

Professional opinion is now almost universally in favour of developing a more strategic, catchment-based approach to fluvial flood alleviation. In addition, there is strong support for the proposed

There are three stages in achieving the aims for fluvial flood-risk management as shown on the right. Each stage requires an understanding of the hydrological, hydraulic, hydro-geological and geomorphological processes at work, flood-defence needs, environmental considerations, planning issues and current and future land use and so on, but at a level of detail appropriate to the stage. The assessment of risks is an integral part of the appraisal process at each stage, to ensure decisions taken at the right time are robust and are based on an awareness of the consequences and appropriate mitigation measures.

Large-scale planning
(catchment flood management plans)

Strategy plans

Solutions

STAGE	CATCHMENT FLOOD MANAGEMENT PLAN	STRATEGY PLAN	SOLUTION
Aim	To identify long-term, sustainable policies to manage flood risk throughout the catchment	To identify appropriate solution types to meet objectives of the catchment flood management plan	To identify the nature of works to implement preferred solution
Deliver	Broad-brush assessment of risks, opportunities and constraints, areas of uncertainty	Preferred approach (i.e. scheme type) including economic and environmental decisions	Comparison of different implementation options for preferred scheme type
Output	Complementary set of generic flood-risk management policies based on MAFF options (e.g. do nothing, do something)	Type of solution (e.g. storage, protection, diversion, land-use change, flood warning)	Type of solution (e.g. flood warning system improvements, reservoir, flood relief channel, reconnect flood plain)

Figure 3.2. Catchment flood management plans are to be implemented as sub-catchment strategy plans delivering specific schemes (reproduced by kind permission of the Environment Agency and Halcrow Water)

programme of catchment flood management plans as a means of delivering this new approach to flood risk management in England and Wales. However, some concerns remain, such as

- the appropriateness of preparing 60–80 catchment plans — would fewer, regionally based, plans be better and is the proposed time-scale for completion of work within three years realistic for such a large task?
- preparation of catchment plans should not delay urgently needed flood defence schemes, particularly for communities that have suffered flooding in recent years
- the focus of catchment plans on flood risk management will, in due course, need to be more fully reconciled with the EU's Water Framework Directive, which embraces the whole water cycle
- whether the proposed three-tier structure (with catchment plans at the top and individual schemes at the bottom) will work effectively — for example, it is usually difficult to choose between options without detailed modelling
- the proposed catchment plan approach is too data and modelling orientated, with too little emphasis on the social, economic and environmental dimensions of flood risk management
- developing and sustaining stakeholder commitment to delivering catchment plan objectives and the related partnership arrangements to implement policies.

3.1.4   Application within the catchment

The strategic policies in each catchment flood management plan may have a role across the entire catchment or may have a different role in the urban, rural, or peri-urban parts of it as they are amplified in the strategy plans for different parts of the catchment.

The catchment-wide role of the catchment plan is to provide not only the data and modelling foundations for the whole flood management process, but also the basis for risk assessment and appropriate management responses to risk. In particular, it will enable the vulnerability of different catchments to flooding to be assessed (based on geology, land use and management, groundwater, etc.) and the effect of future scenarios (e.g. climate change) on

---

Role of Catchment Flood Management Plans (CFMPs) across all parts of river catchments

- Catchment definition.
- Setting up GIS databases for catchment data.
- Arrangements for monitoring catchment processes.
- Identifying appropriate model(s) of catchments.
- Scenario testing (e.g. changes in catchment land use, climate change, extreme events).
- Flood forecasting and warning.
- Definition of flood plains and significant areas subject to non-river flooding.
- Identification of 'key areas' at risk from flooding.
- Relationship of CFMP to statutory development plans and nature conservation strategies.

- the magnitude and frequency of flood events
- the appropriate design criteria for flood defence structures
- the extent of areas at risk.

Urban areas — the emphasis on strategy plans in urban areas is likely to be on managing the social and economic dimensions of flood risk, with environmental issues perhaps secondary. Given that flood defences in many urban areas have been provided in a piecemeal way to different standards, a key role will be to set and then deliver a minimum standard of flood defence together with complementary flood warning and emergency planning arrangements. Integration with urban planning objectives, such as regeneration, will also be important.

Rural areas — the emphasis in rural areas is likely to be on managing flood risk by working with natural processes and promoting biodiversity and sustainable rural development. It is also desirable to direct agricultural and forestry policies, practices and grant regimes towards alleviation of flood risk and to restoring the role of undeveloped flood plains in storing water and reducing peak

Role of CFMPs/strategy plans in urban areas

- Extent of flood risk to existing development.*
- Social and economic profiles of areas at risk.*
- High-level assessment of flood risk associated with potential urban development sites.
- Identify strategic approach to maintenance and renewal of existing flood defences.*
- Identify need for further flood defence measures and preferred approach.*
- Opportunities for urban regeneration arising from flood management initiatives.
- Improving dissemination of flood warnings.*
- Improving effectiveness of emergency planning arrangements.*
- Scope for making existing development more 'flood resistant'.*
- Scope for Sustainable Urban Drainage Systems (SUDS) in new development.
- Strategic maintenance of urban watercourses, culverts, ducts and sewers.
- Location of key infrastructure (e.g. fire stations/hospitals, etc.) and vulnerable development (e.g. rest homes).*
- Areas where 'managed retreat' is appropriate.

These roles will be predominantly urban, but will also be relevant to rural settlements at risk from flooding.

flows downstream. These ideas come together in suggestions for flood storage to be a recognised land use allocated in development plans and promoted to landowners through government incentives to make it an attractive complement to rural land use. The need for a wider social and economic dimension to flood risk management in rural areas is also apparent, with the pilot catchment flood management plan for the Parrett catchment in the Somerset Moors and Levels pointing the way forward.

Role of CFMPs/strategy plans in rural areas

- Management of undeveloped flood plains to restore 'functionality' for storing, or slowing, floodwaters.
- Utilise agricultural and forestry policies, practices and grant regimes to mitigate flood risk.
- Identify opportunities for habitat creation and enhancement to promote biodiversity (e.g. meadow, fen and wet woodland).
- Reduction of soil erosion.
- Water resource and abstraction management.*
- Management of 'ordinary watercourses' away from the flood plain.*
- Location of vulnerable development (e.g. caravan sites).
- Promotion of water quality, fisheries and pollution control, for example during periods of low flow.*

* Conversely, these are predominantly rural but may also have a role in urban situations.

Agriculture in the UK is clearly in distress and the future of subsidies to farming is a European issue. It is important not to promote a myth, since the amount of storage available on the agricultural flood plain is often small in relation to the total flood volume to be accommodated. The government subsidies to land owners and tenants for flood mitigation are not sustainable. For example, one-off capital grants to land owners as part of an overall river basin flood management scheme to maximise the flood plain storage available should be explored, together with the provision of insurance cover for stock and crops damaged by floods.

Peri-urban areas — these are sub-catchments around the edge of towns in which significant built development coexists with large areas of open land, making it distinctive from both urban and rural areas in terms of the flood risk management issues. Depending on the

Role of CFMP/strategy plans in a peri-urban area under consideration for major development proposals

- Provide a high-level assessment of flood risk for major potential development sites.
- Identify any change to flood risk downstream of major development.
- Identify strategic approach to flood risk management in the vicinity of major development sites (e.g. balancing ponds and other SUDS techniques).
- Assist developers in assessing economic viability of development, if financial contributions to flood alleviation works are required.
- Inform preparation of any Environmental Impact Assessment required with a major development proposal.

Good practice in flood risk management: case study C

The Parrett Catchment Project, Somerset: integrated catchment planning to deliver a programme of social, economic and environmental benefits

The River Parrett and its tributaries drain much of Somerset. The lower part of the river catchment is subject to regular flooding, and water management — with all its implications for farming, wildlife and local communities — is a key issue.

The Parrett Catchment Project was set up in March 2000 by local agencies in a pioneering approach that aims to manage flood risk in a more sustainable way by

- developing an integrated flood management plan for the Parrett catchment
- providing a sustainable approach to flood management, including flood defences for towns and villages and the safeguarding of environmental interests, particularly wildlife habitats
- preparing a rural development programme to promote the local economy and social inclusion
- promoting measures to modify land use across the catchment.

Intensive discussions between the project partners (around 20 in all, including the Somerset Levels and Moors Partnership representing the many local parishes in the area) have developed a broad consensus on the way forward. An action strategy was published for consultation in January 2001.

The action strategy provides a long-term vision for the Parrett catchment over the next 50 years, together with project aims and objectives. These objectives will need to be carried forward in a programme of initiatives grouped into three time bands: short (1–5 years), medium (5–10 years) and long term (over 10 years).

Now the key tasks for the Parrett Catchment Project are to develop the partnership into an integrated body that pools its resources and skills to deliver agreed objectives, and to unlock the resources necessary to carry out the agreed programme of initiatives over the coming years.

The project is an important pilot for the forthcoming national programme of preparing catchment flood management plans being promoted by DEFRA and the Environment Agency. It also forms part of the EU's 'wise use of flood plains' project, where it will also help inform implementation of the EU Water Framework Directive.

Further information:

- www.somerset.gov.uk/levels
- www.floodplain.org

specific character of a peri-urban area, the role of the catchment plan and strategy plan may involve a combination of the urban and rural roles outlined above.

There appear to be very few specifically peri-urban roles for the catchment and strategy plans. However, one case would be where such an area was under consideration for large-scale development and a strategy plan could assess the flood risk implications of various development options and the strategic approach to dealing with them.

3.1.5   Future support for catchment flood management plans

There is a clear consensus that the process of preparing catchment flood management plans should be the pivotal initiative in improving flood risk management in England and Wales over the coming years. Accordingly, much is riding on the ability of the Environment Agency to deliver comprehensive coverage in the expected time-scale.

Whereas much effort is rightly going into establishing a sound methodology for preparing catchment flood management plans, producing plans is not an end in itself. More consideration needs to be given to the practical issues of ensuring that there are the leadership and professional skills, stakeholder commitment, partnership structures and financial resources to turn the plans into action on the ground.

There is a critical need to develop a structure of flood risk management that ensures that the sustained leadership and professional skills are available as a high priority and that all stakeholders are brought together in partnership to promote the quality of service to the community in flood risk management.

It should be remembered that the professional skill required often takes eight years of formation, including appropriate academic training in hydrology and hydraulics and river engineering, coupled with an understanding of society's needs and practical experience in applying design skills to solve real problems. Against a background of declining interest in science and engineering, there must be concerted effort to attract and retain professionals and technicians with the necessary interest and skill in river basin flood risk management.

Catchment dynamics
British catchments have long gone through usage changes, and exhibit considerable resilience to these. A prime example is the

building, operation and eventual dereliction of thousands of water mills. Already in existence in large numbers at the time of the Domesday Book that came out of the Norman conquest in the 11th century, they flourished until coal-fired power stations could produce sufficient energy for an embryonic national grid in the early 20th century. Mill development involved countless small head dams, offtake weirs, head leats and discharge channels. A considerable industrial archaeology literature exists about mill water power; none of it indicates that the flood regime of a substantial valley has changed as result of all that activity.

Rates of change of land use may be dramatic on town edges and their associated small drainage areas. However, taken nationally, change is far slower. Remember that excellent hydrological accuracy is plus or minus 2%, and that it is regrettable that so many published values are given to beyond three significant figures. If a rain gauge site is moved it can have a marked effect on its statistical parameters, as too can a change in shelter conditions, or in the way snow precipitation is handled. Observers change over the years, and hence varied skill levels are obtained during a record, even if instrumentation remains unbroken and without the need for repair or replacement. The consequence is that detecting a definite change in the precipitation climate of a region needs concurrence from many sites.

By contrast, flood flow gauging summarises the response of a large area. The associated difficulties of measurement may relate to different issues over the years. These can include changed catchment uses upstream, bed erosion or sedimentation passing unchecked, and new backwater effects from downstream channel changes, such as dredging. Different observing bodies may have adopted new upper-stage rating relationships at irregular intervals, and without necessarily adding back calculations for appropriate application to previous floods.

Controversy never seems to leave the question of whether farmland drainage, which is so extensive in Britain, worsens flood regimes. However, Robinson, of Wallingford's Centre for Ecology and Hydrology, settled the matter conclusively for many when he showed that (Robinson and Rycroft, 1999)

- subsoil drainage of clay land reduces flood peak flow of a given return period by having created a prior storage within the soil zone

- subsoil drainage of sandy land increases flood peak flow by improving the conveyance rate away from a more stable soil water storage.

Naturally such rules imply sensible situations, for example thin soils over rock cannot be expected to have tile or mole drainage applied and sandy soils will only be drained where high water table conditions prevail.

Interestingly, it might be thought that the end of the MAFF grant aid for field drainage would have led to deteriorating farm drainage, due to the lack of funded manpower for its maintenance, and hence to worsening flood regimes. However, it seems from a limited survey by the University of Plymouth that, once established, tile drains can remain running for very many years without sediment or root blockage. Probably the further intensification of British agriculture has ensured that the necessary basic maintenance has been carried out; healthy growing fields are good for flood minimisation whereas bare fields or waterlogged ground is not.

The history of a river's development must be considered when looking at a long flood chronology

- if it became a commercial navigation, it is likely that the occasional rock sill or gravel shoal was taken from the bed, complimenting the construction and modernisation of locks and weirs
- if it is a migratory fish river, it is possible that eel traps were once used
- if it is a gravel bed river, it may have had commercial dredging over key depositing reaches
- if it is groundwater dominated, it may have had a water meadow system fed from head weirs and with the main channel displaced at points to the side of the flat valley bottom, using the relict channel for excess drainage
- if it is a recreational cruising river, it may have marinas in valley alluvium pits through which overbank floods may 'jump' at rare times (a phenomenon that occurred at an old open coal pit in West Yorkshire not long ago)
- if reservoirs of significant volume relative to the flood of concern have been built upstream, the flood regime will have been 'softened' — knowledge of reservoir full status will be needed to confirm whether change in the basic flood propagation will be relevant in each and every event.

Debris supply

The practical gap between the professionals in hydrology and hydraulics has led to clean water flood computations from the former and insufficient appreciation of the uncertainties of calculating flood levels. In 2001, the River Yeo in Somerset was blocked entirely when a harrier jet slid off the RAF Yeovilton runway into its channel. Consider debris supply in its broadest sense

- eroded soil, gravel and even boulders
- sliding saturated peat sheets
- collapsed bridge structures
- floating timber, including bankside toppled trees
- dumped rubbish (shopping trollies being only one example in a range from old cars to minor items)
- displaced riverside caravans
- sunk boats.

The change of landscape has its own influence on flood characteristics. The increase of field size and loss of walls and hedgerows has almost imperceptibly lessened the chance of wave generation by their collapse under flood load. The consequent intensification of arable cultivation has more obviously led to soil displacement downhill in intense rain events, partly aided by longer furrow runs.

Haphazard debris lodging can create scour pockets that undermine key levees or bridge piers. Debris shoals can deflect flow to the extent of causing, in smaller rivers, a new cut across a flood plain meander. Obviously debris damage potential is related to impact energy and blockage afflux; wherever velocity of flow is high there will be rapidly enhanced risk. Wave motion and flow super-elevation is increased, and assessment of freeboard for its containment remains problematic.

Expressing floods in runoff terms

There are many who advocate a return to natural flood plain processes for quelling the impact of rare floods. But is it achievable, and if so, in which type of catchment?

Consider the fundamentals — storm runoff passes through channel and flood plain storage before passing downstream to join other tributary flows. Two conditions are essential if the runoff peak is to be reduced by storage on the flood plain.

1. The storage must be large relative to the rising flood hydrograph volume.
2. The time delay to the peak of the flood leaving that storage must not result in a coincidence of peak flows with those of other downstream tributaries so as to make matters worse than before.

It is known that the first of these is most important, but until the coming of digital flood plain maps it is impractical to take a generalised view of flood plain storage capacities. Reservoir engineers were used to appraise lake storage against spillway flood capacity. Bearing in mind that flood plain size is rarely above 5% of the total area draining to its outlet, there is limited opportunity to hold back much of an extreme flood.

The scale of possibility can be assessed using the Institute of Hydrology (IH) Digital Terrain Model, courtesy of David Morris and Helen Davies at CEH Wallingford. A 50 m grid of UK topography is interpolated from the 50 000 Ordnance Survey contours, after checking for drainage path connectivity with the IH/Environment Agency digitised river network — this ensures the logic of source-to-sea flow routes and enables the triumph of instantaneous basin boundary location that has been achieved by the *Flood Estimation Handbook* CD of catchment characteristics. Table 3.1 sets out some examples of the total volume that is held on a basin flood plain at the peak of a 100-year flood, even assuming the impossibility that all

Table 3.1. *Undefended flood plain capacities at 100:1 chance flood peak*

River	Flooded area in 1% flood: % of catchment	Mean depth: m	Equivalent runoff: mm
Tees	4	0·22	8
Witham	23	0·14	31
Thames	8	1·33	27
Welsh Dee	5	0·22	11

reaches can experience flood peak level at the same time. It can be seen that flat valleys store proportionately more than steep ones, that geological controls on valley width are very important, and that the size of storage compared with the 100-year flood peak discharge varies markedly when expressed as a ratio of that stored volume. Table 3.1 assumes that all defences are overtopped or bypassed, i.e. it gives the maximum possible stored value *if* every defence were to be 'retreated' by 'clearing the flood plain' (as some advocate).

Thus, at the peak of a 100-year flood on a hilly catchment, only about 10 mm of the excess rain is in storage. On lowland catchments this figure may be three times larger. The implication is that washland redevelopment of the original flood plain has more hope of (modest) success in flatter catchments, as one would expect. The trial values above are not immediately obvious, even to experienced flood hydrologists. Expansion to cover all basins above 100 km^2 would be useful, as would interpretation by geomorphologists of the flood plain depth variations.

Instead, compare a dedicated flood storage reservoir of 10 000 ML, which is large in UK reservoir safety terms. That equates to only 1 mm of stored runoff over 10 000 km^2, the catchment of the Thames — if that reservoir is placed so it captures 10% of the catchment it still only holds 10 mm runoff, and has far less impact further downstream. Flood storage of that type is best reserved for the Tonbridge/Ashford situation, where it is placed immediately above the town needing protection.

These sums are not an academic exercise. If the intelligent lay public are aware of a rising overbank flood, then hear a weather forecast of 'another 25 mm tonight on saturated ground', but know that the local flood plain occupies 5% of the catchment, they can soon realise that the average flood rise to be expected is about 25 mm/5% = 500 mm.

Allan Lambert's paper on 'Catchment models based on iso-functions' (Lambert, 1972) demonstrated his command of the Dee storage/outflow relationship for use in real time flood management. Sadly, it seems not to have been followed up elsewhere.

Table 3.2 shows the relative rates at which a sample of major English and Welsh catchments can shed water at the height of the rarest flood recorded in the National River Flow Archive; it assumes that the flood-of-record given in the latest volume of the *Hydrometric Register and Statistics* (NERC, 1997) for each of these basins approximates the 100:1 chance flood — if anything the true 100:1 flood peak will be higher, based on the typical length of record available to the National River Flow Archive (http://www.nwl.ac.uk/ih/).

It is possible to see, at a glance, that when a certain size of storm rainfall is forecast to fall on a saturated basin it will, or will not, cause a further build up of flood plain inundation. Further thought will reveal why some basins are prone to long intermittent rain-day sequences whereas others, generally smaller, will only react adversely to individual storm days.

Lay understanding of flood outcomes could be improved further if the Meteorological Office would broadcast the river flood flow rates as mm/day. So, for example, the 100:1 chance flood peak of the Thames at Teddington is around $1000 \text{ m}^3\text{s}^{-1}$ or 9 mm/day runoff from the basin; the layman has more hope of understanding the latter, particularly when the next predicted daily rainstorm is clearly above that value and so the flood must rise further.

It will require a change from what is the current forecast practice of (vaguely) predicting the possible high point of storm rainfall moving in to 'south-east England'. Instead, it is vital that catchments are named and areal average storm rainfalls given. Why cannot the public be given the more detailed forecasts that the Environment Agency receives, either by Ceefax/Teletext or on the internet? Fishermen have access to river stage recorders over the phone; why can there not be real time access to flood stage records across key points in Britain, all available freely on the internet? The WHYCOS system of the World Meteorological Organisation (WMO) does just that at a growing number of points elsewhere in the world, for example

- http://medhycos.mpl.ird.fr/en/t1.php?ime=data/td.inc&gr= data/acc/&gn=dat.inc&menu=data/md.inc
- for Victoria http://www.vicwaterdata.net/isc/pics/mainjpg.jpg
- for the USA http://water.usgs.gov/realtime.html

The last of these is the most comprehensive. The biggest challenge is to keep any such system going when overloaded at the time of a flood crisis.

Table 3.2. Flood-of-record runoff rates

River	Event	Flow: m^3/s	Area: km^2	Expressed as mm/day
Tyne	13/10/1967	1586	2176	62
Wear	05/11/1967	577	658	75
Tees	03/01/1982	417	1264	28
Hull	29/03/1979	18	378	4
Yorkshire Ouse	05/01/1982	622	3315	16
Aire	01/04/1969	340	1932	15
Don	23/06/1982	201	1256	13

Table 3.2. continued

River	Event	Flow: m^3/s	Area: km^2	Expressed as mm/day
Trent	26/02/1977	1006	8231	10
Up. Witham	11/02/1977	38	298	11
Welland	10/03/1975	78	717	9
Nene	18/03/1947	382	1635	20
Bedford Ouse	15/03/1947	278	1460	16
Little Ouse	30/03/1979	24	699	3
Wensum	28/04/1981	37	536	6
Gipping	02/02/1979	45	311	12
Essex Stour	18/09/1968	44	844	4
Roding	22/11/1974	62	303	17
Lee	17/03/1947	118	1036	9
Thames	18/11/1894	1059	9948	9
Medway	04/11/1960	295	1256	20
Gt Stour	09/04/1979	38	345	9
East Sx.Rother	09/12/1965	52	206	21
Sussex Ouse	22/11/1974	129	396	28
Arun	12/01/1972	94	379	21
Itchen	19/12/1982	18	415	3
Test	11/01/1961	37	1040	3
Avon	19/09/1978	100	1706	5
Dorset Stour	28/12/1979	280	1073	22
Frome	26/02/1966	24	414	5
Axe	27/12/1979	244	289	72

Table 3.2. continued

River	Event	Flow: m^3/s	Area: km^2	Expressed as mm/day
Exe	04/12/1960	493	601	70
Teign	30/09/1960	313	380	71
Dart	27/12/1979	550	248	192
Tamar	28/12/1979	715	917	67
Fowey	27/12/1979	127	169	65
Camel	27/12/1979	228	209	94
Torridge	28/12/1979	730	663	95
Taw	04/12/1960	650	826	68
Tone	11/07/1968	113	202	48
Yeo	27/12/1979	139	213	56
Som. Frome	10/07/1968	108	262	35
War. Avon	11/07/1968	371	2210	14
Severn	01/01/1982	641	9895	5
Wye	20/03/1947	905	4010	19
Usk	27/12/1979	945	912	89
Taff	27/12/1979	652	455	123
Neath	27/12/1979	323	191	146
Tawe	27/12/1979	461	228	174
Tywi	21/03/1981	702	1090	55
E Cleddau	12/12/1964	199	183	93
Teifi	27/12/1979	303	894	29
Dyfi	12/12/1964	581	471	106
Conwy	12/12/1964	510	345	127
Clwyd	26/09/1976	82	404	17
Welsh Dee	14/12/1964	665	1020	56
Weaver	08/02/1946	212	622	29

Table 3.2. continued

River	Event	Flow: m^3/s	Area: km^2	Expressed as mm/day
Dane	04/01/1983	135	407	28
Irwell	27/10/1980	485	559	74
Mersey	09/12/1983	423	660	55
Douglas	09/10/1983	49	198	21
Ribble	27/10/1980	1221	1053	100
Wyre	08/12/1983	191	275	60
Lune	02/01/1982	854	983	75
Kent	21/12/1985	276	209	114
Leven	02/12/1954	136	247	47
Cum. Derwent	01/10/1968	265	663	34
Eden	24/03/1968	690	1367	43
Lyne	30/10/1977	293	191	132

3.2   CATCHMENT MODELLING

3.2.1   Role of catchment modelling

Catchment modelling provides a very powerful tool which, to date, has been relatively underused, especially within flood estimation and management. With the advent of catchment flood management plans and the EU Water Framework Directive, the shift from local, site-specific management to catchment-scale management offers an ideal opportunity to demonstrate clearly the benefits that can be achieved by using models.

The strategic principles concerning flood alleviation at a catchment scale have been summarised in Section 2.4, and the drawing up of strategic Catchment Flood Management Plans

(CFMPs) are described in Section 3.1. Although primarily concerned with floods here, it should be recognised that droughts as well as floods may affect many of the issues described next when drawing up general Catchment Management Plans (CMPs).

CMPs are intended to relate strategic issues governing sustainable development and environmental concerns at a river basin or catchment scale. The topography of each catchment essentially defines the drainage pattern by way of streams and rivers in such a way that the volume of potential water falling as precipitation (i.e. rainfall/hail/snow) within the catchment stays within that catchment and may be accounted for in various ways by way of, for example in broad terms, evapotranspiration, surface runoff or groundwater flow. Thus, CMPs are a means of relating the flux of water through a catchment to the many practical issues related to that catchment, such as

- water resources
- drainage capacity
- flood mitigation
- economic development
- land use
- planning controls
- flood plain development
- transport planning
- environmental concerns
- pollution control
- nutrient supply
- aquatic habitats
- river corridor ecology
- alluvial morphodynamics.

These issues typically touch on a wide range of political and environmental objectives and, as such, demand multi-objective management.

The concept of multi-purpose river basins in the UK was first enunciated in 1871 by Lord Montague who argued that: 'The various interests on land and river, navigation and mills, drainage and water supply, fishing and manufacturers, can be adjusted and developed only by one management over the whole river' (Bailey, 1991). This well-founded concept of river basin management has survived the many changes to river management in the UK over the last 125 years

(Knight, 1996a), and will assume an even greater significance in the UK and Europe through the implementation of the EU Water Directive (2000).

Models, as with any other tools or controls, are not a panacea and will not provide all the answers. What they can provide is a means to improve the understanding of catchment processes.

CMPs, CFMPs and river basin management rely heavily on the use of 'models' to explore the response of the catchment to specific rainfall scenarios, consequent excess runoff, resultant water levels and possible flood defence options. Models are essentially a description of 'how things work' and a mathematical model is commonly described as 'a set of general laws or mathematical principles and a set of statements of empirical circumstances' (Hempel, 1963). In describing water flow through a catchment there is a need therefore to link a variety of fluids models based disciplines such as

- meteorology and hydrology
- hydrology and hydraulics (hydrodynamics)
- surface water and groundwater
- geomorphology and ecology.

A popular misconception is that our understanding of the physical processes at work in each of these disciplines is now at such a sufficiently advanced state so that all we have to do is to select and join together appropriate models in such a way that a seamless whole will emerge, thereby giving a complete description of the spatial and temporal movement of a flood wave throughout a particular catchment. It is important to appreciate that this is not so, because of some of the inherent scientific and philosophical limitations in the modelling process. Before dealing with the different types of model, the following Section (3.2.2) attempts to illustrate briefly some of these limitations to modelling in the two crucial disciplines regarding flood movement, namely hydrology and hydrodynamics.

To ensure effective river basin management, models must be used to explore the response of the catchment to specific rainfall scenarios, consequent excess runoff, resultant water levels and possible flood defence options, requiring the combination of hydrology and hydraulics.

The main modelling area of direct relevance to flooding is that of hydrodynamics, where the catchment hydrology is related to the channel hydraulics to predict flooding. However, since the introduction of the 1975 *Flood Studies Report* (NERC, 1975), there has been an increasing disconnection between these two disciplines, which must be addressed. The relationship between rainfall and runoff has generally been regarded as an essentially hydrological problem. Hydrologic modelling has become the prime focus of flood investigation, with the prediction of the design flow being the main goal. The design flow is now most frequently determined using the methods in the 1999 *Flood Estimation Handbook* (CEHW, 1999). But, as stated, the reliance on such methods does not readily allow for future predictions where catchment and climatic changes can occur.

3.2.2   Limitations to modelling

The relationship between rainfall and runoff has generally been regarded as an essentially hydrological problem (Beven, 1996; Moore and Bell, 2000; O'Connor, 1995 and 1997; Shamseldin, 1996; Shaw, 1994; Woolhiser, 1996). Despite many decades of research, no agreement has yet been found among hydrologists concerning the most appropriate rainfall–runoff model. Indeed, some of their leading researchers are on record as saying: 'no such "perfect" model exists which will perform well on all catchments, at all times and in all circumstances' (O'Connor, 1997), 'for predicting streamflow, physics-based models presently offer no advantage over conceptual models and present a computational disadvantage' (Ye *et al.*, 1997), and 'it cannot be assured that distributed models are based on the correct equations to describe hydrological reality at the grid scale' (Beven, 1996).

3.2.3   Hydrological modelling

Taking the rainfall–runoff issue as an example, there are three broad types of model.

- Lumped empirical *black-box* runoff model (systems based).
- Quasi-physical *conceptual* runoff model (dominant mechanisms based).
- Distributed *physically based* runoff model (individual mechanisms based).

In the 'lumped empirical black-box runoff model' there is no attempt at modelling individual processes, and reliance is placed on the empirical discovery of transfer functions in the time domain between input (usually rainfall) and output (usually discharge). The 'black-box' may have changed colour to a 'grey-box' in certain circles, following systematic development.

In the 'quasi-physical conceptual runoff model' there is crude attempt at simulating the dominant processes on the basis of a relatively small number of elements each of which is itself a simple representation of a physical relationship. Dooge (1977) states that 'some conceptual models can be regarded as representing mathematical approximations to the system response obtained by black box models'. Conceptual models not only lack scientific realism, which limit their operational success, but also the 'information carrying capacity of the available data may be inadequate to allow the effective calibration of a complex conceptual model with adequate precision in a physically meaningful sense' (O'Connor, 1997).

The 'distributed physically based runoff model' is based on the most general partial differential equations in three space dimensions and time, with the term 'distributed' referring to the space dimension. Relating continuum equations to a catchment is therefore problematic, given the heterogeneity of the medium (surface and sub-surface), the discretisation of the physical parameters which will not be smooth in space or constant in time, and the consequent 'lumping' of parameters at a computational scale which becomes increasingly important as the scale of computation extends to encompass an entire catchment. The physical basis of distributed models is therefore an issue, as is their accuracy, since over parametization often leads to inappropriate calibration and use. It is clearly difficult, if not impossible, to calibrate models with a multitude of interacting parameters, many of which are not yet even physically measurable with any degree of certainty. Antecedent conditions that govern the initial and boundary conditions in hydrologic models are also important (Webster, 1998). Some have even argued that distributed models are 'trans-scientific, and that simpler models should be used' (Woolhiser, 1996). It might also be argued that solving the continuum equations by finite difference, element or volume is inherently adopting a 'lumped' approach to parameters at the grid scale in any case.

There is a wealth of literature on comparative hydrological model performance (e.g. Bell et al., 2000; Moore, 1999; Moore and Bell,

2000; O'Connell, 1991; O'Connor, 1997; Perrin *et al.*, 2001; Andersson, 1992; Shamseldin *et al.* 2001; Todini, 1993; Ye *et al.*, 1997, to name but a few). The World Meteorological Organisation (WMO) publishes regular comparisons (e.g. WMO, 1992) and academic journals abound with examples. A recent notable intercomparison study is that by Perrin *et al.* (2001), who compared the performance of 19 lumped rainfall–runoff models using the daily data of 429 catchments located around the world. They generally found that 'the complex models outperform the simple ones in calibration mode, but not in verification mode' (Perrin *et al.*, 2001). The same conclusion may also be found in the literature concerning distributed models, where as might be expected from the philosophy inherent in the approach, they perform well in general at a small scale, but not so well at a large scale. This naturally arises from the embedded equations that purport to simulate the flow physics in the model, which have been derived from 'simple' conditions. For example, the use of Darcy's law for saturated flow, based on tests in a homogeneous laboratory medium, does not necessarily relate to conditions at a geological grid scale (fractured aquifers, soil moisture values varying with land use, etc.). As Woolhiser (1996) concludes, 'At best we might say that for intermediate and large watersheds simpler models will give equally bad answers at a lower cost'.

There are also obvious difficulties in comparing models based on differing philosophies and technical bases to a relatively small number of the many millions of catchments worldwide. Every catchment is unique, despite certain similarities, and no amount of modelling will reveal all the hydrological parameter possibilities in real life. Topographical and meteorological similarities may reduce the number of parameters and amount of modelling required, but even the concept of 'pooling', adopted in the *Flood Studies Report* (NERC, 1975) and *Flood Estimation Handbook* (CEHW, 1999) for flood frequency estimation, raises other concerns.

Even these comparative model studies, however, may be of limited use, since most only concentrate on the causative rainfall and the consequent runoff, usually prescribed as discharge at some specific site(s). There is generally no consideration of the variations of internal catchment parameters in space and time by direct measurement. Thus, the emphasis is usually on obtaining a single parameter output through global discharge or flux balancing. As in all models, the quality of the input data, and the variation of all state variables during simulation are of primary importance in validation. A model may give a 'good' result for the wrong reasons. The issue of the amount of data that is required to validate a model, and how the process of validation should be carried out raises other issues. The question posed by Beven (1996), 'what would be the minimal model to describe a distributed response?', is worth considering, as is the dilemma about the intrinsic worth of pursuing a purely 'reductionist' approach to natural phenomena. In the context of the distributed model versus conceptual model debate, it seems that 'the resolution does not lie in ever more detailed descriptions and ever more demanding requirements for data collection for parameters and state variables' (Beven, 1996). Thus, rather than build ever more complex distributed models, it may well be appropriate to use a relatively simple model with fewer parameters. This effectively takes the distribution of responses into account, rather than using a lumped description at the element scale. The same philosophy is evident in meteorological models, which previously used lumped descriptions of land surface hydrology within elements up to 300 km in scale (Beven, 1996). This 'disaggregation' approach is in contrast to the approach adopted by other researchers. Abbott *et al.* (1996) argue that 'the problem of over-parametization', should be overcome by 'avoiding making too many degrees of freedom in connection with calibration procedure. Hence, almost all distributed data should be data which are not subject to calibration'.

Finally, it should be recognised that as catchment scale models for determining the flux of water throughout a river basin continue to improve, so does the likelihood that they will be used for purposes outside flood hydrology. When combined with appropriate hydrodynamic surface and groundwater sub-surface models, the distributed model may be extended to a multiplicity of uses related to topics such as ecohydraulics, sediment transport, channel morphology, geochemical studies, pollutant dispersal, nutrient supply, aquatic growth, etc., as well as for the primary purpose of satisfying water resources requirements. Despite the power of remote sensing, data capturing programs and GIS, a good understanding of the physical processes and possible model limitations are two essential prerequisites for all modellers (Figure 3.3).

3.2.4   Hydraulic modelling

Somewhat similar philosophical and technical limitations also exist with models in hydraulic engineering. This is especially so with

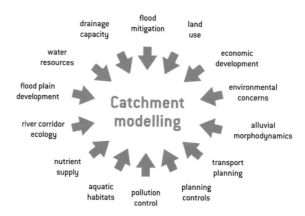

Figure 3.3. Improved catchment models could have much wider use than flood management

models concerned with rivers, as indicated by the following quotation (Simons, 1992)

> Hydraulic engineers working with fluvial systems must recognise and avoid pitfalls associated with the use of mathematical models and expert systems (artificial intelligence) without full knowledge of their strengths and limitations.

The current state-of-the-art in the various branches of hydraulics is well described by Nakato and Ettema (1996), in river mechanics by Knight, (1996b), and in hydraulic modelling by Abbott and Basco (1989).

Fluid flow analysis in river channels and on hill slopes is generally based, but not exclusively so, on the following three broad types of model

- *Physically based* hydrodynamic model (one-dimensional, two-dimensional and three-dimensional versions)
- *Stochastic* model (random process based)
- *Conceptual* model (dominant process based).

In the 'hydrodynamic' model, the fluid flow is represented by the three-dimensional Reynolds' averaged Navier-Stokes (RANS) equations. It should be noted that the simpler Navier-Stokes equations for laminar flow have no known general closed-form solution, and are regarded as one of the seven chief mathematical problems of the 21st century. A US$1 million prize awaits the solver of these equations. Adding the phenomenon of turbulence, enunciated by Reynolds mathematically in the 19th century, leads to the RANS equations, governing all fluid flow phenomena. These equations then have to be solved by numerical methods. Despite 150 years of study, turbulence is still regarded as one of the most intractable problems in the physical world, due to its random nature and complex structures.

Stochastic models attempt to avoid the 'deterministic' nature of turbulence closure models, and may be based on general principles of entropy, chaos theory or statistics. Conceptual models in hydraulics are somewhat similar to those in hydrology, and focus either on the transfer function for relating key parameters in a dominant process or on a simplification of the governing hydrodynamic equations. The aggregate dead zone (ADZ) model for pollutant dispersion is a good example of the former type, and the one-dimensional kinematic or convective-diffusion type of flood routeing models are examples of the latter. Both types of model are frequently used as sub-models in distributed hydrological models. The level of linkage between hydrodynamic and hydrological models is not necessarily as straightforward as some assume. At a fundamental level, a certain amount of similarity may be noted between the deterministic approach adopted in both the distributed hydrological model and the hydrodynamic turbulence model. However, it is clear that until the latter, with simulation for all turbulence phenomena, is fully incorporated in the former, then there is no such thing as a complete distributed rainfall–runoff model.

In order to solve the RANS equations numerically, additional partial differential equations are required to describe the distributions of Reynolds' stresses and turbulence phenomena, leading to what is known as the 'turbulence closure' problem. Different turbulence closure may be obtained by way of a number of different approaches, such as eddy viscosity, k–ε model, giving some representation of anistropy, the k–ω model, a two layer model with k–ω near the boundary and non-linear k–ε elsewhere, large eddy simulation (LES) and direct numerical simulation (DNS) (see Nakato and Ettema, 1996). All of these are technically difficult, even for flow in simple geometries, but when applied to rivers with a free surface there are considerable technical problems. DNS is well beyond the range of current computing resources, except possibly for NASA and Boeing.

Simpler levels of closure are therefore inevitably adopted in all models applied to rivers, which are more problematic than the simpler geometrical shapes found in aero or mechanical engineering. Rivers have boundaries that are not only topographically variable, but also have heterogeneous roughness and, in some cases, boundaries that are deformable (e.g. sediment) and are themselves flow dependent (e.g. ripples, sand dunes and bars).

Assuming that the flow physics of a river may be reduced to a certain level of description, the application to a specific site requires the selection of a certain spatial type of model (one-dimensional, two-dimensional and three-dimensional versions), the selection of an appropriate grid (shape and size), the adaptation of the grid to the physical boundary, the selection of a type of numerical procedure (finite difference, element or volume) and the selection of input parameters and state variables within the cross-section or along the reach. The schematisation of the river itself is also a feature that is often neglected, and may still rely heavily on routine survey or extraction of data from digital terrain maps. Ideally, the specification for the location and detail of the input cross-section survey data should require a good understanding of the turbulent flow mechanisms induced by particular topographical and boundary features. For example, understanding the turbulent flow structures in a meandering channel (Sellin *et al.*, 1993), may indicate where survey sections should be positioned in the first place. It is only after all these procedures have been followed, is it then technically possible to link flood discharge with flood water level. In hydraulic engineering, it is well known that it is quite possible to obtain the 'right' answer for the total discharge through a particular river cross-section, but have the flow distribution and turbulent parameters incorrect (Knight and Shiono, 1996). Such errors can be particularly important when, for example, determining the amount of water flowing over a flood plain, or when calculating the distribution of boundary stress in the river channel for estimating sediment transport or erosion/aggradation rates. Issues related to research and development in hydrodynamic and hydrological modelling are discussed further in Section 7.7.

3.2.5 Types of model

Specific examples of the broad types of hydrological and hydraulic model described in Section 3.2.1 may be found in textbooks and papers. Some have developed incrementally from earlier models of a similar type, whereas others have developed historically from new insights or driven by new needs. A selection of well-known models and their approximate date of origin/key development might include the following.

Hydrological models

Black box types. The rational method (Mulvaney, 1850) is a simple empirical formula that relates the storm runoff peak to the previous constant (or mean) rainfall divided by the time of concentration of the catchment. This method probably has the longest record of continuous use by the engineering and hydrological profession in the UK.

The unit hydrograph method (Sherman, 1932), relates the excess or effective rainfall (i.e. the total rainfall minus the losses) and the storm runoff (i.e. the total discharge minus the baseflow). The description of the Instantaneous Unit Hydrograph (IUH) by a two-parameter gamma function by Nash (1957), using a reservoir cascade, opened the way to linking catchment characteristics with the IUH through a linear time invariant system. Dooge (1973) reviews other attempts at establishing such links.

Conceptual and distributed types. In the light of the discussion in Section 3.2.2, these are considered together. One of the earliest successful conceptual models is the Stanford Watershed Model (Crawford and Linsley, 1966), which uses daily rainfall, a simple infiltration function and a combination of unit hydrograph and recession function to produce the mean daily discharge. In all quasi-conceptual models, which are either lumped or semi-distributed, it should be noted that 'the effects of the spatial averaging of the inputs and the heterogeneity of the catchment characteristics are integrated in the rainfall–runoff modelling by the spatial probability averaging the processes occurring at an elementary area or point to yield a description of these processes at a catchment scale' (Shamseldin, 1996). Many other conceptual models have been developed along similar lines. See also Shaw (1994) for further details on models.

The Systeme Hydrologique European (SHE) model, developed jointly by the CEH (formerly the Institute of Hydrology), the Danish Hydraulic Institute (DHI) and a French consulting company (SOGREAH), solves the non-linear flow equations from overland

and channel flow, unsaturated and saturated sub-surface flow to provide a physically based distributed system approach to the catchment (Abbott *et al.*, 1986). The surface flow is treated as being two-dimensional, with no complete turbulence representation. As indicated earlier, the model requires a significant number of parameters and, consequently, there is an incompatibility between the scale of measurement and the scale of the computation. It is therefore strictly a 'lumped' model. The Institute of Hydrology (now CEH) also has its own distributed model, known as IHDM, described elsewhere (Calver and Wood, 1995). A more flexible approach to a physically based distributed model is the quasi-physical conceptual TOPMODEL, a TOPography based MODEL, which has a set of conceptual tools that can follow the responses of the differing contributing units (Beven *et al.*, 1984). The flexibility of the model, and its reliance on fewer parameters gives it some advantage over more parameterised deterministic models.

Hydraulic models

The basis of different types of river model may be found in many textbooks and occasionally in the user manuals of commercial software packages. Some examples are as follows.

One-dimensional models.   In these cases the river is represented as a one-dimensional system via cross-section data, and the software (e.g. ISIS, HEC-RAS MIKE11 and HYDRO-1D) solves the one-dimensional hydrodynamic (St Venant) equations for mass and momentum. Sinuous channels are represented by way of curvilinear streamtubes, and additional head losses at particular structures, such as bridges, weirs and sluices, are taken into account by ancillary equations, usually based on energy coefficients. Flow over embankments and through the flood plain is taken into account by spill equations. Despite the gross simplifications of the physical process, one-dimensional models can provide quite reasonable estimates of water level and can be a useful design tool. They may also be extended into a quasi-streamwise flow two-dimensional model, with some three-dimensional effects included by the use of individual panel averaging.

Two-dimensional models.   In these software (e.g. TABS2, TELEMAC2D and SSIM), a depth-averaged form of the RANS equations are used, with appropriate simplification to the turbulence phenomenon. The advantage of such models over the equivalent one-dimensional models is their ability to describe direction as well as magnitude in both the river channel and on flood plains. Like most two-dimensional coastal models, the averaging in the vertical direction presumes a logarithmic law for the streamwise velocity distribution, with eddy viscosities computed accordingly. Lateral interfacial shear between adjacent streamtubes is based either on standard one-dimensional equations or not at all.

Three-dimensional models.   As mentioned in Section 3.2.2, since turbulence modelling is predominately still in the research environment, there are only a few commercial three-dimensional software packages (e.g. TELEMAC3D, CFX, PHOENICS, FLOW3D and HYDRO-3D). These have been developed mainly for the mechanical and aeronautical engineering market, and the take up by other branches of engineering, notably chemical and civil engineering, has lagged somewhat behind. It is likely that significant strides will be made over the next few decades to utilise such models more in fluvial engineering. They will not necessarily replace all other lower dimensional models, but will be used where especially needed, and be coupled with one-dimensional and two-dimensional models elsewhere. As always in river engineering, one does not need a sledgehammer to crack a nut, and 'the right tool for the right job' is a sensible maxim to remember and practice.

3.2.5   Future modelling issues

Both the roles of hydrology and hydraulics are important in flood analysis. In essence, hydrology models give the discharge, Q (i.e. the runoff from the land), at a particular location, and hydraulics gives the water level or 'stage', H, at that location (via hydrodynamic modelling) and, hence, water levels along the downstream stretch of river and its associated flood plains. The link between stage, H, and discharge, Q, is of particular importance. Methods such as those in the *Flood Studies Report* (NERC, 1975) and the *Flood Estimation Handbook* (CEHW, 1999) tend to ignore the role of hydraulics and this imbalance must be rectified if progress is to be made in modelling flood phenomena in a catchment.

Distributed hydrological models and hydrodynamic turbulence models contain numerous parameters that, in some cases, are either unknowable or not capable of being measured. There is therefore a need to recognise the uncertainty in the predictions given by all such models. An estimation of uncertainty should be undertaken concurrently with model predictions, by using an appropriate methodology (e.g. the Generalised Likelihood Uncertainty Estimation (GLUE) method of Beven and Binley (1992)).

The climate change scenarios from the Intergovernmental Panel on Climate Change predict that Britain will experience more frequent weather extremes and, in particular, more frequent intense rainfall events. In this context, historical data are of significant value, but we need to look at more innovative methods of flood estimation, including modelling, if we are to manage flood risk successfully.

Distributed hydrological models and hydrodynamic turbulence models contain numerous parameters that, in some cases, are either unknowable or not capable of being measured. There is therefore a need to recognise the uncertainty in the predictions given by all such models. An estimation of uncertainty should be undertaken concurrently with model predictions, by using an appropriate methodology (e.g. the GLUE method).

There is a danger that with a more complex model there is both less flexibility and understanding of the total response of the river or catchment to a particular type of input. Modellers and forecasters in particular need to adapt and customise existing models, and therefore need to understand them fully. It should also be recognised that large models tend to stifle initiatives, to produce 'tunnel' vision and, furthermore, there is always the danger that the software becomes 'institutionalised'.

A recent review of EU-sponsored research and technological development on flood hazard summarised some important conclusions concerning river basin modelling in the following terms (Casale, 1998)

> many models and modelling systems are available for components of river basin modelling. Progress will be made by integration of models across the disciplines involved

> there is a danger that the end-user requirements of models will move beyond the fundamental capability of the conceptualisation and numerics of the calculation 'engines'

> a topic of particular concern is the need to model processes and integrate data at different temporal and spatial scales according to

the application and this will increase as modelling is used to explore the impacts on flooding of long term environmental change.

In fact, the range of models is not as large as stated, as some types are not appropriate. The cost of upgrading models is demonstrably high, arising form either the inclusion of new methodologies or shifts in conceptualisation philosophy. The ambitions of modellers are likely to keep changing and outstrip current concepts and methods. Greater use is likely to be made of holistic models for purposes outside flood analysis. Further details of the extensive EU studies on the impact of climate change on flooding and sustainable river management are contained in the proceedings (5 volumes) of the River Basin Management and Flood Mitigation (RIBAMOD) programme. The final workshop of the RIBAMOD programme (Balbanis *et al.*, 1999) makes numerous conclusions relevant to this report, and should be studied in detail.

The quality of model output depends not only on the model but also the modeller. There is an increasing trend of models being used by those not familiar with them. Modellers divide now into 'developers' and 'non-expert users'. There is a trend to use models as one does software, such as spreadsheets. There is a vulnerability when non-experts use a model mechanically that they do not have an understanding of what the model actually does and what its limitations are and, as such, cannot qualify results satisfactorily. It is also important that both the developers and non-experts need to interface with practical experience to improve their understanding of real conditions.

4 Urban drainage

Charlie Rickard

4.1 URBAN ENVIRONMENT AND FLOOD RISK

4.1.1 Background

The transformation of vegetated land to impermeable surface has gone hand-in-hand with the development of our urban areas over the past two millennia. This has led to a substantial decrease in the proportion of rainfall that infiltrates into the ground and a consequent increase in surface runoff, in terms of both volume and flow rate. Initially, this problem was overcome by the digging of surface drainage ditches to convey the excess flow to the nearest natural channel but, in the last century, there has been a dramatic increase in the adoption of piped drainage systems to convey surface (and foul) drainage from the affected areas.

In parallel with this has been the 'urbanisation' of the natural drains and streams around which the urban areas grew. Perhaps the two most significant forms that this took were concrete lining and culverting, both of which led to environmental degradation of our streams. Culverting also resulted in a finite limit to the flow capacity, and greatly increased the risk of blockage.

Much of the work of piping and culverting drains and sewers in urban areas was carried out as a result of the Public Health Act 1936. This legislation was implemented in good faith, and with considerable improvements to the quality of life in the urban environment. However, in many cases there was no provision for maintenance of the buried assets created, and (understandably) little appreciation of the rapid expansion of the urban environment that would be experienced within the lifetime of these assets.

In the present urban environment, surface water runoff is often diverted into 'combined sewers', which in dry weather carry only foul flow. These sewers were, and still are, designed to accommodate the runoff generated by relatively common storm events — up to 5–1 chance flood in any year (20% annual probability of flooding or 5-year return period). These are short-duration events because the rain finds its way into the sewer system very quickly from the impermeable surfaces. In such storms, the volume of runoff is generally not large and the storage available in the sewer system when full ensures that flooding is avoided for more severe rainfall events, perhaps as severe as a 50–1 chance flood (2% annual probability of flooding or 50-year return period). This certainly does not apply to all sewers (Figure 4.1). The expansion of the proportion of catchments that have a predominantly impermeable surface and the likely impacts of climate change will ensure that storm water sewers are under an increasing risk of being overloaded. Storm water sewers also become overloaded as a result of sustained rainfall, such as that experienced in the winter of 2000.

Figure 4.1. Sewer flooding in River Street, Truro, in October 1988

4.1.2   Sewer flooding

Urban drainage is the responsibility of the water companies in England and Wales and the regional water authorities in Scotland, soon to become one national water authority. Since the privatisation of the water industry in England and Wales, sewerage undertakers (usually the water plcs) are required to keep a record of incidents that result in internal flooding of properties (referred to as 'DG5' incidents). Funding levels are set at five-year intervals by the Office of Water Services (OFWAT) to carry out the necessary improvement works to reduce the risk of such incidents occurring.

OFWAT's records for the three financial years from 1997 to 2000 (OFWAT, 2001) provide information on the number of properties flooded in each year, as well as the number of properties considered to be at risk of flooding once in ten years and twice in ten years.

In the year 1999/2000, around 3800 properties were flooded due to overloaded sewers and 3350 as a result of blocked sewers or equipment failure. These figures were up by 36% on the previous year, although the overall figures for properties at risk are considerably down on those reported in the early 1990s. Overall there are presently estimated to be 8660 properties at risk of flooding twice in ten years and another 17 960 once in ten years. These numbers of flooded properties are comparable to the total number flooded in the autumn 2000 floods, and cannot be disregarded. However, due to their spread in time and location, they do not attract the same media attention.

For example, Southern Water plc has approximately 560 properties at risk. This does not perhaps suggest a major problem. However, it is understood that the recent periodic spending review (OFWAT, 1999) only allows for the investment of £1 million over five years to cure this type of problem. At an estimated £50 000 per house to cure the problem, this level of investment will only solve the problem for 20 houses (less than 4%) and it seems highly likely that more houses will come under risk in the five-year period concerned. There is therefore considerable cause for concern at the low level of investment to overcome the risk of sewer flooding.

The problem is compounded by the fact that the water plcs have limited control over the water that is discharged into their sewers. Sewerage legislation gives people the right to connect into a sewer, even if it does not have the necessary capacity, and there is a similar right to discharge surface water into a sewer. There is legislation that provides for the developer to contribute to the cost of upgrading sewers, but this is not always followed. This unfortunate situation is also complicated by the fact that water plcs are not statutory consultees in the planning process. It is clear that current sewerage legislation needs to be reviewed with sewer flood control in mind.

Human rights and public authorities

A recent legal case (*Peter Marcic* v. *Thames Water Utilities* [May 2001]) determined that Thames Water had potentially violated human rights as a result of allowing a sewer to flood Mr Marcic's home many times over a period of nine years. Thames Water argued that it would cost £1 billion to rectify all such problems and that this could only be paid for by increased public contributions. The judge took this into account, but decided that there was still an unjustifiable interference with human rights. It seems likely that this judgment will put increasing pressure on the water plcs to address the DG5 flooding incidents, and this will clearly require a reassessment of the spending restrictions determined by OFWAT.

Water also finds its way into the sewerage system from groundwater and from overflowing highway drains. In conditions when flooding has come from rivers or other watercourses, it is also common for manholes to be lifted in an attempt to alleviate the problem — and this results in sewers being overloaded. In extreme floods, such as those observed in the autumn of 2000, flooding via sewers as a result of backing up from the river outfall, or the failure of sewage pumping stations as a result of flooding, becomes more of a problem.

4.1.3   Urban channels

The decline in our urban streams and brooks (Figure 4.2) has gone largely unnoticed by many, especially where these have been

Figure 4.2. A typical urban channel — most are poorly maintained and prone to blockage

culverted (out of site, out of mind). Although most of them no longer act as conduits for foul sewage (thanks to the 1936 Public Health Act), many are treated as a convenient disposal system by local residents. Everything from plastic bags to garden prunings and from traffic cones to shopping trolleys finds its way into these urban streams, with consequent risk of blockage and environmental decline (Figure 4.3).

Many of these channels are the responsibility of the local authority and are poorly maintained due to competing demands on the available funds. Furthermore, many authorities no longer have their own drainage teams as a result of pressures to out-source some of the services that they traditionally provided. This is not an environment that encourages investment in urban drainage, especially since the channels appear to function adequately for much of the time. It also reflects the difficulty of specifying maintenance standards in out-sourcing contracts.

Although DEFRA (as MAFF) introduced *High Level Targets for Flood and Coastal Defence* (MAFF, 1999b) in November 1999 for the inspection and recording of the condition of flood defence assets, this requirement has been ignored by many local authorities so there is inevitably a degree of ignorance about the present condition of these assets. The *High Level Targets*, insofar as they apply to the local authorities, concern non-main rivers. A rural local authority may have thousands of kilometres of these watercourses, only limited lengths of which are classified as 'critical ordinary watercourses' (i.e. having an identified flood risk to life or property).

Bybrook Barn Garden Centre Culvert, Kent

In January 2001, the Court of Appeal overturned the decision of a lower court and decided unanimously that Kent County Council was responsible for nuisance when a culvert on Bockhanger Dyke proved inadequate in the storm of 12 August 1996. Leave to appeal to the House of Lords was refused.

The council's predecessor had built the culvert around 1950. Almost inevitably there has been development in the catchment since that date. Nevertheless, it appears that a culvert owner can be responsible in law for future and unforeseen flood damage, even though construction was by some earlier owner.

The decision is a specific interpretation of an occupier of land having a duty of care about reducing risks to a neighbour. That duty requires an owner to do all that is reasonable; that duty becomes more onerous on an owner with the expertise and financial resources to manage the asset well, in this case a Highway Authority.

It seems likely that what is reasonable will involve regular inspection, appropriate maintenance and technical adjustment of the structure to meet current flood protection standards. These standards can be either those of society in general, or those used by the owner at other comparable sites.

Figure 4.3. Shopping trolleys and traffic cones are often found in our urban channels — cars are a little less common!

4.2   ANALYSIS OF THE PROBLEM

The causes of flooding in the urban environment include

- culvert, drain and gully entry blockage (partial or total)
  - dumped rubbish
  - floating debris, including leaves and branches
  - sediment deposition
  - hailstone drift
- poorly maintained urban watercourses (silted up, overgrown with vegetation, or blocked with rubbish)
- bridge, culvert or tunnel waterway capacity exceeded
- failure of drainage pump, or jammed sluice gate
- high water level in receiving river that flows back up the drain or sewer
- sewer manhole broken open to create a drainage route, or cover lifting off due to over-filling

- balancing storage, fills and spills into a channel no longer able to accept the 'natural' flood event
- rising groundwater levels, both seasonal and longer term.

All of these occur as a result of heavy rainfall that generates runoff. Short duration, high-intensity storms, which can occur at any time of year, tend to cause localised problems. More widespread flooding occurs as a result of prolonged rainfall, and rain falling on rural catchments that are already saturated from rainfall in the preceding days or weeks. This latter situation characterised the floods of autumn 2000, which were extreme to the extent that they affected a large part of the country at one time.

New developments constructed on low-lying land present particular problems in terms of the provision of sewerage services (lack of head for gravity drainage) and the effectiveness of sustainable urban drainage systems (risk of high groundwater levels). Such low-lying sites are therefore not only at risk of river flooding but may suffer from sewage flooding due to the backing up caused by high river levels, or groundwater flooding due to prolonged above-average wet conditions. These factors need to be taken into account when assessing the merits of developing any particular site.

4.3   DEVELOPMENT OF SOLUTIONS

4.3.1   Urban watercourses

There can be little doubt that our urban watercourses are often a neglected resource. There are exceptions but in many urban channels there is clear evidence of litter and debris, dilapidated concrete and brick walls and silted up and overgrown beds. As a result, these streams and drains are unattractive and inefficient conveyors of floods. The frequent presence of culverts on many reaches may overcome the adverse visual impact, but the risk of blockage and the associated risk of flooding are worsened.

Notable steps to reverse the situation have been made. However, the time has now come to recognise these urban streams more widely for what they are and to seek to improve their environmental status at the same time as improving flood conveyance. This will be difficult unless parallel steps are taken to reduce the volume of runoff from the urban and rural catchments, because reintroduction of more natural

Figure 4.4. In the future we will face some stark choices. These will include the option of returning some urban channels to a more natural regime, and relocating houses and other buildings out of the flood risk area (photograph from Mott MacDonald archive)

features in the channel is likely to reduce flow capacity rather than increase it. A good example of such a scheme is that proposed for the Quaggy, which runs through the London Boroughs of Bromley, Greenwich and Lewisham. In this scheme the traditional approach of straightening and concrete lining the channel has been abandoned in favour of a river restoration approach (CIWEM, 2001).

We should not shy away from reclaiming urban channels that have been culverted or encroached upon by development. This will require space, and may mean the loss of gardens and even demolition of properties, but it may be the only viable solution in some instances (Figure 4.4).

In view of the high risk of flooding caused by blockages of culverts and trash screens, it is important that all critical culverts are assessed for this risk. Use should be made of the recently completed research and development project on the performance of trash screens (Environment Agency, 2001c). Further research and development work on the subject of blockages within culverts should be considered.

However, it must be accepted that reducing the risk of obstructions from one part of the system may simply pass the problem downstream, with similar consequences in a different location.

At the present time, there is an arbitrary division of responsibility between the Environment Agency and local authorities for the management of flood risk from urban watercourses. Rivers and streams designated as main river are the responsibility of the Environment Agency, and the remaining watercourses are the responsibility of the local authorities (except for some agricultural drains in low-lying areas that are the responsibility of internal drainage boards). The designation of main river is intended to reflect the importance of the channel as a main conveyor of drainage flow, but there are many other channels not so designated that pose a real and recurrent risk of flooding. This division of responsibility is reflected in the lack of a comprehensive database of flood defence assets, the lack of which inhibits good management of these assets. It also causes confusion to the public, and complicates both the delivery of flood defences and the provision of an emergency response in the event of a flood. It is time for this division of responsibility to be resolved.

Culvert Design

Culverts provide one of the most common forms of drainage structure. They range in scale from a short length of 450 mm diameter pipe under a farm access track, to multiple steel or concrete constructions capable of carrying a large stream under a motorway. A culvert can extend for hundreds of metres under industrial and residential developments, and is often ignored, even neglected, until a flooding problem acts as a reminder of its existence. A significant number of the culverts constructed over the past 100 years have been poorly designed, badly maintained, inappropriately extended, or simply do not have adequate capacity for today's conditions. It is not uncommon to find that older culverts are obstructed by, for example, a foul sewer that has been constructed at a later date and passes across the culvert barrel.

Nowadays the culverting of natural channels is discouraged by the Environment Agency, not only because of the hydraulic problems that culverts can cause, but also because of the environmental loss. Where a culvert is required it is important that the designer appreciates all the potential problems and takes them fully into account in developing his solution. Comprehensive guidance is available from the CIRIA *Culvert Design Guide* (CIRIA, 1997). Some fundamental guidance is given below.

Size is important
The culvert must have sufficient capacity to carry the design flow safely, generally with free surface flow. It should be large enough to convey freely all debris carried by the stream (see following box on the need for, and design of, trash screens). Culverts smaller than 450 mm diameter should be avoided, even on the smallest of drainage channels, as they are so easily blocked by silt or trash. A single barrel is preferred to multiple barrels, so that the barrel cross-section area is maximised for debris conveyance, and to facilitate inspection and maintenance.

Low flow is important too
Most of the time the flow in the culvert will be small in relation to its capacity. This can lead to sluggish flow and sedimentation. The designer should consider the full range of flow conditions and try to design the culvert to match conditions in the natural channel. The provision of a low-flow channel within the culvert, or a lower invert in one barrel if the culvert is multi-barrelled, will help to keep sediment in suspension.

Steps and bends cause problems
Steps, bends and changes of cross section should be avoided as they complicate the hydraulic design, cause additional head loss, and can trap debris. Such features are common in older culverts where alterations and extensions have been carried out over the years. If these cannot be avoided, provide a manhole at the change to allow inspection, and ensure that the change in section is streamlined as much as possible.

Remember — a culvert is for life!
The design of the culvert should take into account its performance over the expected lifetime (60 years). This means anticipating changes that could lead to increased flows (it is very difficult to increase the capacity of a culvert once it has been constructed). It also means considering very carefully the inspection and maintenance requirements, and making sure that the design does not frustrate or complicate these activities.

Trash and security screen design

It is very easy to design a screen that will prevent trash, debris, and children from gaining access to a culvert. Such a screen will remove the fear of death of adventurous children, and will ensure that the culvert will not block with trash. However, a poorly designed screen runs the risk of rapid blockage in high flows, leading to damaging flooding of homes, factories and infrastructure (Figure 4.5).

The best advice is often to avoid a screen if at all possible. Although culverts do pose a safety risk to children, the same is true of roads and railways, and it will never be possible to prevent all accidents. The decision to provide a safety screen should therefore be based on a thorough assessment of the real risks, and not just a knee-jerk reaction.

If it is decided that a security screen is required, it should be designed as if it were a trash screen, because it will inevitably collect trash. The spacing between the bars should be as wide as possible (to reduce the accumulation of trash and debris) but not more than 150 mm (so as to prevent children from gaining access).

All trash screens collect trash and therefore need to be inspected and cleaned on a regular basis. Debris accumulation

Figure 4.5. Trash screens in front of culverts can easily block in a flood

is most rapid in flood flows, when rapidly rising water levels pick up loose material, such as fallen tree branches and litter. Floods often occur at night and in inclement weather, therefore safe access for inspecting and cleaning the screen is vital.

The area of the screen should be a multiple of the area of the culvert — between three and nine times depending on the anticipated debris load (note the screen area is measured in the plane of the screen up to the flood level). The height of the screen should not exceed 2 m for any element, so that safe raking is possible (see Figure 4.6). The angle of the screen to the horizontal should not be more than 60°, and should preferably be 45° to allow debris to ride up the screen with rising water level. Intermediate platforms should preferably be formed from open tread flooring so that they are free-draining, non-slip and contribute to the available flow area.

The screen should be formed from robust galvanised steel members so that damage by vandalism is minimised. Screen bars should be braced where necessary using recessed members that cannot obstruct the raking process. The screen should be provided with a lockable hatch to allow access for inspection and maintenance. Safety of operatives should be considered, including the provision of custom-made rakes, and the building-in of anchor points for the attachment of safety harnesses.

Above all, the person or organisation that will be responsible for ensuring that the screen is kept clear must be made aware of the operation and maintenance duties that the presence of the screen will impose.

Figure 4.6. Trash screen on the outlet form the Bourne Ditch flood storage reservoir, Windsor — note the two-stage arrangement and provisions for easy access to allow safe inspection and clearance of accumulated debris (photograph from Mott MacDonald archive)

4.3.2   Urban sewer systems

The huge value that we derive from our urban sewer systems should not be underestimated. In general they work extremely well in removing foul and surface water, so much so that the average person remains largely unaware of their existence. There will, of course, always be occasions when these sewers let us down, and there is real cause for concern that recent expenditure has focused on environmental improvements (to water quality) at the expense of increasing flood risk. This bias needs to be examined in the light of the recent spate of flood events and taking account of the likely adverse impacts of climate change.

There is also some cause for concern that the interaction between rivers and streams and the urban sewerage system is not adequately considered in the development of major urban flood alleviation schemes. This requires greater emphasis, since the flooding of homes by sewerage backed up by high river levels is likely to increase in response to both urbanisation and climate change (Figure 4.7).

There is also evidence to suggest that under-designed highway drainage systems can lead to sewer flooding when the resulting surface water finds its way into the foul sewerage system.

There is a clear need for a more integrated approach to flood risk management between the water plcs and other main parties involved, namely the Environment Agency and the multitude of local authorities. This should lead to a reduced risk, for example by ensuring that strategic sewage pumping stations will continue to operate even if there is heavy river flooding in the area.

There has been considerable research in recent years into leakage from sewers, mainly driven by environmental concerns. However, leaking sewers also allow water to flow into the pipe in conditions of high groundwater. Since such conditions are likely to become more common in the future, there is a need to carry our further research into ways of ensuring that this does not lead to an increased risk of sewer flooding.

Modern methods of sewer analysis have encouraged the use of attenuation techniques to reduce peak flows. Further work is needed to develop our understanding of design storms (profiles, critical storms and multiple peaks) and of the implications of designing sewers to overfill or 'surcharge' (Figure 4.8).

More research into the interaction of sewer and piped drainage systems and the rivers into which they discharge in flood events is

Figure 4.7. Overflowing drain on housing estate

Figure 4.8. Surcharging sewerage system

needed. This is an area of research that inevitably falls between two stools, requiring collaboration between the DEFRA/Environment Agency research and development programme and UK Water Industry Research (UKWIR). It is understood that the UK water industry is commissioning a three-year research project into the effects of climate change on sewerage systems. This study should include an assessment of the role of sustainable urban drainage systems and the impact of more frequent and longer duration river floods on sewers and sewage pumping stations.

4.3.3 Sustainable urban drainage systems

In recognition of the growing problem created by the expansion of impermeable surfaces in our urban areas, and the piping of runoff from them, there has been considerable interest in alternative approaches that are designed to reduce runoff rates. Such alternatives are commonly referred to as sustainable urban drainage systems, or SUDS (CIRIA, 2001). The main types of approach being considered are

- diverting runoff from impermeable surfaces to soakaways
- making hard surfaces (such as parking areas) permeable
- creating temporary storage for runoff (e.g. in ponds or underground storage tanks)
- incorporating 'swales' — wide, shallow sloping drainage ways — that have the attributes of storage, local conveyance and infiltration.

Many of the options being considered also have environmental advantages, such as the removal of pollution (reed beds) and amenity value (ponds and wetland areas).

Although sustainable urban drainage systems have been mainly targeted at new developments, some application of the techniques in existing urban areas is possible. There is also a strong case for greater use of such systems to reduce flows from highway runoff. The systems can have added benefit in terms of reduced risk of major river pollution incidents (Figure 4.9).

Although benefits can be achieved by the use of sustainable urban drainage systems, they cannot provide a solution to all runoff problems. Better design guidance is needed on basic hydrological

Figure 4.9. Part of the sustainable urban drainage systems installations at Welcome Break's Hopwood Park Services on the M42 — Spillage Interceptor Basin (photograph courtesy of HR Wallingford)

assumptions, performance of infiltration systems and maintenance requirements. In particular, the following issues need to be addressed

- inapplicability of infiltration systems in areas of low-permeability soils
- reduction in effectiveness after prolonged periods of heavy rain when detention ponds are full and/or infiltration potential is reduced or lost due to saturated soils or high groundwater levels
- reduced effectiveness in the winter as a result of frozen ground
- risk of blockage of small-scale flow control devices (a soft-drink can lodged in a balancing pond orifice was reported to have caused flooding of a house)
- destabilisation of slopes in steep areas (saturated soil conditions)
- the possibility that delaying runoff from a particular site will result in a coincidence of flood peaks in the receiving channel

- the long-term performance of infiltration systems that could become contaminated with oil or silt
- the overloading of undersized piped drainage systems in the event of failure of sustainable urban drainage systems
- general siltation of ponds and other storage facilities.

None of the above should inhibit the use of sustainable urban drainage systems in a cautious manner. Many of the concerns will only really be fully addressed through the monitoring of actual installations, and this is where future research effort should be concentrated.

There has been some constraint to progress as a result of the reluctance on the part of local authorities or water plcs to accept responsibility for maintenance of sustainable urban drainage systems. The reasons for this are clear — there is considerable uncertainty about the long-term performance of these systems. This needs to be addressed by the government, and suitable measures taken to overcome it, if necessary by a change in the law.

It should also not be forgotten that piped drainage systems will continue to play an important role in the future. Their disadvantages of limited capacity, liability to block, and rapid delivery of water to the receiving watercourse, should be weighed against the considerable advantages that they offer.

4.3.4 Sewer and drainage system design and modelling

The use of sewer design software is well established. However, there is evidence to suggest that the design storm profiles need to be revisited to ensure these accurately reflect climate change and improved data. This work is already being undertaken by UKWIR.

In the case of sustainable urban drainage systems, there is a need for more guidance on the design approach, particularly in terms of the design storm (intensity and duration). In particular, recent moves by the Environment Agency to insist on limiting runoff from developed sites to 'greenfield' runoff is too restrictive (see box overleaf). Guidance is also needed to cover the eventuality of failure of sustainable urban drainage systems, either due to overloading in an extreme storm or as a result of long-term degradation.

Runoff from a hypothetical development site

Gross site area is 10 hectares of which 3 hectares is developed (100% runoff) and 7 hectares is undeveloped (30% runoff). The proposed new development will increase the developed area to 6 hectares and reduce the undeveloped area to 4 hectares.

Table 4.1. Analysis of runoff from a hypothetical development

	1 hour	24 hour
Rainfall statistics: mm		
Annual storm	6.2	25.5
1% probable storm	45·6	110·0
Runoff: m³		
Present situation:		
annual storm	316	1301
1% probable storm	2326	5610
Future situation:		
annual storm	446	1836
1% probable storm	3283	7920

Table 4.1 presents the results of an analysis of runoff from a hypothetical development site for which there are proposals to increase the developed area. The calculations show the increase in runoff generated by the proposed extension to the developed area, for two storm durations (1 hour and 24 hour), and two probabilities (the 'annual' storm and the 1% probable storm).

Recent Environment Agency guidance on such development proposals has suggested that runoff detention (flood storage) should be provided to ensure that the drainage flow from the future developed site should be no worse in the 1% probable flood than it is at present *for the annual flood*. This guidance is offered without any reference to any particular storm duration.

For this requirement to be met, the storage volume that would have to be provided on the site would be as follows

- 2967 m^3 if based on the 1 hour storm, or
- 6619 m^3 if based on the 24 hour storm.

Until recently, guidance was normally based on the concept that the development would not *increase* the drainage flow from the site for the 1% probable storm. This would require the following storage on site

- 130 m^3 if based on the 1 hour storm, or
- 2310 m^3 if based on the 24 hour storm.

The latest guidance is flawed in that it does not specify a storm duration, and it is open to challenge in that it implies a substantial betterment. This is not to say that betterment in terms of reduced runoff from developed sites is not a good idea, but it is not necessarily appropriate to penalise new development by imposing such stringent requirements. The provision of on-site storage can be expensive, and there are often practical limitations, especially if the stored water has to be evacuated by pumping. It is therefore important that current guidance is reviewed, and a clear policy is developed that is rational and sustainable.

4.3.5 Scope for flood alleviation measures in historic towns

Where historic towns have been subject to flooding, and flood alleviation measures are under consideration, sensitive design is required so that the defences are successfully assimilated into the historic environment. This may make flood defences more difficult, or more expensive, to provide. For example, some people may feel that traditional flood walls or embankments may adversely affect the character of a conservation area or the setting of listed buildings. Alternatively, it may be necessary to use higher grade materials — such as brick or stone facings on sheet-piled river walls — to integrate a flood defence scheme successfully into the historic environment.

Recent technological advances provide another alternative in the form of 'demountable' flood defences in very sensitive locations. This type of defence would only be erected when flooding is threatened. During the majority of the year, when the river is not a threat, they are simply not there. They can be used on their own or on top of a low flood wall, so there is room for flexibility in their use. However, demountable defences can take around eight hours to erect, so will not be suitable in catchments where rivers respond quickly to heavy rainfall.

Historic centres often contain vacant sites or buildings in the flood plain, which become the subject of planning applications for residential or commercial development. If acceptable in principle within the terms of *Planning Policy Guidance Note 25, Development and Flood Risk* (DTLR, 2001), the Environment Agency normally seeks raised floor levels, or putting habitable rooms on upper floors, to mitigate flood risk. While this advice is sensible in terms of managing flood risk, it can present considerable design problems in integrating the proposed development into a historic street. Artful design can often, but not always, reconcile conflicts between conservation and flood risk objectives.

The fitting of flood resistant products (such as flood doors, guards or skirts) to historic buildings must be done sensitively, so that they do not damage the special interest or integrity of the historic structure. Emerging guidance from English Heritage advises that 'in particular, the existing structural systems and materials must be respected; the materials and techniques used should be traditional and compatible with the existing ones; and any alterations should be detectable and reversible'. The advice goes on to say that 'it is important to keep a sense of proportion — flood proofing works should be designed according to realistic assessments of the likelihood and severity of flooding'.

Opportunities for sustainable urban drainage systems in historic areas will be limited by their existing densely developed character and by the relatively small sites which come up for redevelopment. However, there are small, simple ways in which sustainable urban

Groundwater flooding

Over the past 25 years there has been significant drive to construct more and more houses to meet a growing demand. This has put pressure on local authorities to allow the development of sites that, in the past, had been avoided for good reason. The obvious result has been the much reported encroachment onto the flood plains of our rivers and streams; but this is not the whole story.

There are many parts of the country where there is a less obvious potential source of flooding — one that tends to lie dormant until we experience a run of wet years. In such circumstances, long forgotten springs and seeps appear, transforming otherwise ideal development land into marsh and bog.

One such site was reported recently in the *Times* (19 June 2001). At Chase Field in Farringdon, Hampshire, a development of 16 houses was subjected to severe groundwater flooding when springs reappeared in December 2000. Flood depths reached as much as 1 m in the houses, and the waters did not recede for six months.

With hindsight, it is possible to determine that this site was at risk. Indeed, planning permission was refused in the 1950s for, among other reasons, 'liability to flooding'. An examination of historic documents also supports this, with references to springs as far back as 1822.

Such incidents reinforce the need to look at all possible sources of flood risk when considering development proposals. Groundwater flooding tends to persist long after surface waters have receded, and the solutions to the problem can be difficult and expensive.

Historic maps and old place names can provide a useful insight into groundwater flood risk in any area. Words such as 'spring' on a map, and place names like 'Boggy End' are clear warning signs that should lead to a thorough investigation of the risk.

drainage systems principles can be applied. For example, instead of using hard surfacing for car parking spaces or footpaths, gravel can be used to promote natural drainage.

Lastly, lest it be thought that managing flood risk in historic areas is a succession of conflicting problems, it must be emphasised that it also offers opportunities for regeneration. The case of Gainsborough in Lincolnshire, where provision of flood defences has been a catalyst for regeneration of a historic town, is a good example

4.3.6   Development in flood risk areas

Where appropriate, planning authorities should require a 'drainage impact assessment' for all new developments as advocated in *Planning Policy Guidance Note 25, Development and Flood Risk* (DTLR, 2001). This would cover all drainage related issues in sufficient depth to ensure that appropriate and sustainable solutions are incorporated into the development proposals. However, we need to avoid placing too onerous requirements on developers in terms of reducing the runoff from new sites. The following example illustrates the point.

Where new development is allowed in areas where there is a flood risk, it will be appropriate to require that the houses and other buildings have some degree of resistance to flooding. These flood resistance requirements would also apply to developments on the fringes of the flood plain and to developments within defended areas, although to a lesser extent.

The development of flood-resistant buildings (see Section 5.4.3) is already the subject of an ongoing research project, but the building industry should be actively encouraged to develop and advertise innovative approaches to reducing the impacts of flooding on buildings.

5   *Engineered solutions*

Charlie Rickard

5.1   ROLE OF ENGINEERED SOLUTIONS

The picture painted by the media in the autumn and winter of 2000 was one of failure of the nation's flood defences in the face of severe climatic conditions. Whereas it would be wrong to underestimate the damage and human misery caused by the floods, it should be emphasised that engineered flood defence works protected tens of thousands of homes that would otherwise have been flooded (see Figure 3.1).

Flood defence engineering is as old as the history of urban civilisation itself and the some of the basic solutions, such as flood embankments (or dykes), have changed very little over the centuries and will remain appropriate for the future. Indeed, some flood embankments, now over 400 years old, are the very essence of a sustainable approach to flood risk management (e.g. the Barrier Banks that contain the Ouse Washes flood storage area in the Fens of East Anglia — see Figure 5.1). This is not to say that such solutions will remain sustainable in the future, especially in the face of climate change and rising sea levels. For the future it is clear that we need to explore a much wider range of options, so that the most appropriate solution can be found, based on a full appreciation of

- the environment in which the defences will be constructed
- the impact that the defences will have on both the local and the wider environment
- the performance of the defences in a wide range of flood events
- the risks and uncertainties involved.

Figure 5.1. Flood embankment raising in the Fens of East Anglia has provided a sustainable solution for 400 years, but it cannot go on forever (photograph from Mott MacDonald archive)

Furthermore, the decision as to whether to proceed or not must be based on a full assessment of (in order of priority)

- the social need (rather than some political imperative)
- the economic case (rather than the financing opportunity)
- the environmental consequences (rather than formal impact mitigation).

It is important to recognise that engineered flood defences will continue to provide one of the main options for flood risk management for the foreseeable future.

5.2   SUSTAINABILITY

There are many definitions of sustainability but essentially the aim is 'to provide for today's needs without compromising the ability of future generations to meet theirs'. The constant reference to sustainability into today's world implies that we have been acting in a non-sustainable manner in the past. In the context of flood defences this is hardly true in the sense that most existing fluvial flood defence

Figure 5.2. The Leigh Barrier on the River Medway in Kent creates a regulated flood storage area to protect the town of Tonbridge

schemes would be classified as sustainable over the next few generations. However, continued development of such schemes is in danger of compromising future generations unless the full implications are assessed and addressed now.

The most sustainable of solutions are likely to be those that address the issue of runoff at source. The introduction (or reintroduction) of storage into the rainfall–runoff relationship can be particularly effective when applied near to the point where runoff begins. Storage is also very effective further down the system if it is sufficiently large in proportion to the problem, as has been demonstrated beyond doubt in the recent autumn 2000 floods (e.g. Leigh Barrier on the River Medway (Figure 5.2) and the Lincoln Washlands).

The least sustainable of options include further raising of flood defences to constrain a river 'within bank', or the construction of new defences to provide protection to new urban areas on the flood plain (Figure 3.1). Such solutions generally worsen the problem for other riparian land owners or developments and it would be easy to say that they should only be considered when no other option is viable. However, this is too simplistic and the quest should be to find a solution that suits each particular case. Otherwise, successful schemes such as that for Gainsborough, which combined flood risk management with a parallel need for urban waterfront regeneration, might not have gone ahead. This highly commendable scheme was completed just in time to ensure that the inhabitants escaped the misery that was visited upon 10 000 less fortunate people in autumn 2000 (Figure 3.1).

The longer term sustainable option is to let rivers have space in urban areas and to encourage the development of an urban river corridor that can accommodate increased flood capacity in sympathy with the urban use of the land.

5.3 GETTING THE BALANCE RIGHT

The secret of flood risk management is getting the balance right. This requires weighing the needs of people against our desire to conserve the environment, while also taking into account other demands on the public purse, including health and education.

One major initiative that will help us to conduct this delicate balancing act is the move away from a focus on local solutions to a broader, catchment-wide approach to flood risk management. In this regard, the adoption of strategy studies as a basis for developing solutions along our major rivers, and the more recent initiative of catchment flood management plans, are to be welcomed. However, in addition to thinking globally there will be a continuing need to act locally by providing engineered solutions. A particular area for further study is the link between land use and flooding, so as to have confidence in policy changes that could lead to a significant reduction of flood risk. It is recommended that whole-catchment modelling be undertaken with greater vigour to address this issue.

In the autumn 2000 floods, it was apparent that in many of the locations that were flooded only a small number of properties were affected (Environment Agency, 2001d). In Wales, for example, at 182 of the 211 locations that were flooded, less than ten properties were flooded. It was a similar story in the Anglian Water region, where out of 40 locations, 37 had five or fewer properties affected and none had more than ten. This tends to suggest that flood proofing (i.e. making buildings more resistant to flood damage) and localised flood mitigation measures may form an important part of flood risk management in the future.

In circumstances where it is appropriate to provide engineered defences to protect significant numbers (i.e. hundreds) of people in a community, the aim should be to provide a high standard of defence even if the economic analysis reveals that a lower standard would yield a larger benefit-cost ratio. This is already the case in statutory reservoir safety policy. It is recommended that the target should be based on providing standard protection against the 100–1 chance flood (1% annual probability of flooding or 100-year return period) as a minimum. Lower standards would only be adopted where there was overriding justification for doing so and not, as at present, because (for example) a 75–1 chance flood standard gives a higher benefit-cost ratio. Nor is it acceptable to have adjacent flood defences constructed to different standards justified solely on the basis of the benefit-cost ratio.

These protection standards are presented in the traditional 'event-based' terminology that has driven our approach to flood risk management for the past 50 years. This should not be interpreted as a plea to continue this approach for the next 50 years. We are now in a much better position to take a broader view of flood defence, allowing us to examine the performance of schemes for a wide range of flood events, and testing the sensitivity of the solutions to variations in the basic assumptions. This process will allow us to be more confident in the schemes that are proposed and implemented, especially in terms of their performance in extreme flood events.

Whereas it will never be possible to guarantee protection against all floods, our aim should be to provide flood defence schemes where these are sustainable and can be economically justified, with a target standard of protection of the 100–1 chance flood.

A town in the south-west has a current standard of protection for a 2–1 chance flood (50% annual probability of flooding or two-year return period). It has been flooded five times in the last three years. A 25–1 chance flood (4% annual probability of flooding or 25-year return period) standard could be achieved for an investment of £0.5 million. The 100–1 chance flood (1% annual probability of flooding or 100-year return period) standard could be obtained by the construction of a flood storage scheme, but would cost twice as much.

Both options have acceptable benefit-cost ratios. There are more easily identified environmental concerns about the storage option but it is a clear winner in terms of the standard of protection provided and it brings with it the positive benefits gained from flood storage. Under current rules, funding will only be provided for the 25–1 chance flood scheme.

In such cases there should be a balance in favour of the human factor, and the 100–1 chance flood scheme should be funded.

In the case of existing heavily urbanised areas and for new developments in flood risk areas where there are over-riding reasons to develop, the balance should be tilted back in favour of human safety and technical soundness rather than environmental impact.

The performance measures for DEFRA's *High Level Targets for Flood and Coastal Defence* (MAFF, 1999b) are

- the number of lives lost through flooding
- the aggregate benefit-cost ratio for grant-aided schemes (the aim is to achieve 5–1 or better).

Whereas the desire to reduce lives lost is clearly laudable, the only other identified indicator is a strictly economic measure. The addition of another performance indicator, namely the number of households damaged and distressed by flooding in a year, will provide a valuable indicator of the extent of the problem. This will help to drive down the number of flooding incidents that cause distress to people and damage to property every year.

With respect to grant aid, there is a perception that the 'level of proof' required by DEFRA in support of an application for grant aid is unnecessarily onerous for the level of funding available. In addition, there seems to be an ethos of 'fine tooth combing' submissions, rather than accepting them for what they are. The *Lessons Learned Report* (Environment Agency, 2001a) notes a

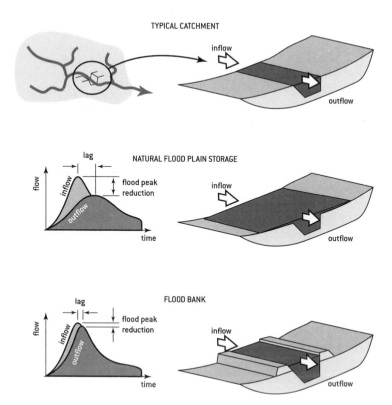

Figure 5.3. Constraining a river within higher banks reduces the flow reduction offered by the flood plain (adapted from Fleming (1975))

perception that DEFRA's 'benefit-cost decision rule leads to a reduced standard of defence at a time of increased uncertainty such as climate change and changes in catchment characteristics'. This focus on the benefit-cost ratio needs to be redirected to take more account of the human dimension.

5.4   AVAILABLE OPTIONS

This book is not the place to present a treatise on the options available for flood defence. However, it is useful to identify the key options and discuss their particular merits. Fundamentally, there are two basic options for dealing with excess flow in rivers

- temporary storage
- flow passed downstream.

The essence of these two main options is clearly illustrated in Figure 5.3.

5.4.1   Storage options

General
Water is stored in all parts of the catchment and river system as part of the natural process of conveying rainfall to the sea. Solutions that encourage temporary storage of flood waters are mimicking nature and, where practical, are to be preferred. The process of identifying storage options should start at the source of runoff. Such approaches have been developed in other countries, notably the United States, but also in third-world countries where water conservation rather than runoff reduction is the aim.

Storage on farmland
Within the river system itself, replacement of lost flood plain will help to redress the balance. There is no doubt plenty of scope for this in rural areas, where farmland has been isolated from the river in the past to increase agricultural production. However, wholesale removal of low flood banks protecting farmland might worsen the situation downstream, by allowing the flood plain to fill early in the development of a flood. There is thus a need for caution in the assessment of such proposals. The introduction of strategy studies and catchment flood management plans with associated hydraulic models will allow the impact of agri-environmental schemes to be fully explored as an element of flood risk management for the whole river.

The concept of set aside to encourage desirable habitats in place of unnecessary agriculture is well established. A similar principle can be applied to flood plain areas, or potential flood storage areas, to encourage farmers to allow seasonal or periodic flooding of selected land areas. However, riverain lands are likely to be the more productive areas, and compensation levels may have to be higher. Given a free choice, a farmer will generally choose a lower yielding upland area for set aside, and continue to farm his riverain land which may well be protected against flooding. It is clear, therefore, that such decisions cannot be made in isolation. It is hoped the creation of the new Department for Environment, Food and Rural Affairs, with responsibility for agriculture, environment, and flood defences in both urban and rural areas, will be the catalyst for a more holistic approach to solving these problems.

It is worth noting that the Royal Society for the Protection of Birds (RSPB) is presently working with the National Farmers Union (NFU) to develop a voluntary payment scheme to landowners who offer up their land for multi-purpose washlands in four pilot schemes. It will be important to monitor the success of such schemes in terms of their impact on flood risk reduction.

Regulated flood storage reservoirs
Where on-line or off-line storage schemes are proposed in the future, these should be seen as opportunities for environmental enhancement and amenity improvement. However, it would be a mistake to assume that such storage schemes should always be constructed around the concept of a wetland habitat. There will be opportunities for schemes where the storage area provides amenity space (e.g. the Bourne Ditch Scheme in Windsor — see box on the next page) or agricultural production (e.g. Lincoln Washlands) when not being used for flood storage. Perhaps the best example of this is the Ouse Washes, in which the flood storage area also serves to provide grazing land, wildlife habitat and amenity value.

There is also the possibility of the joint use of water supply reservoirs with flood storage. This is not widely used due to many problems at present, but it will come into focus with the Water Framework Directive and catchment flood management plans and should not be overlooked as a potential tool.

River restoration
Restoring our rivers to a more natural state is another means of water storage, through the slowing down (and hence backing up) of the flow through the river reach concerned. Such techniques have been successfully applied in flat countries, such as Denmark, and they are being tried out in this country albeit on short reaches. We should certainly pursue this type of approach wherever appropriate but it is unlikely to offer a complete solution. River restoration should be part of the whole process, with other measures being taken to reduce runoff and temporarily store water so that the restored river is not itself a cause of flooding. As such, river restoration is much more

Flood storage — design and operation

The design of main river flood storage schemes requires a full understanding of the hydrology and hydraulics of the river system to ensure that the optimum use is made of the available storage. The most fundamental issue is the question of when the flood storage reservoir starts to fill. If the process starts too early, there is a risk that it will be full before the peak of the flood arrives, and flooding downstream occurs as a consequence. If the filling commences too late, the flood peak may be missed, and the flow passing downstream is not reduced enough to avoid flooding. This delicate balancing act was demonstrated in autumn 2000 when the Leigh Barrier on the River Medway was operated to fill the storage area in just five hours, thereby saving Tonbridge from severe flooding (Figure 5.2).

The simplest of flood storage schemes are those that mimic nature, whereby flood waters flow onto the flood plain when the river level overtops its banks. The construction of low embankments along the river, designed to overtop on average once or twice in ten years or so, allow agricultural activity to continue on the flood plain in most years. Floods that would threaten downstream towns and infrastructure cause overtopping of the banks, and the storage created reduces the risk of flooding downstream. Such 'informal' storage schemes are common on many rivers in England and Wales (for example, the upper reaches of the Severn, where the embankments are locally referred to as *argaes*). These schemes operate automatically when the river level reaches the bank top level. It is important that the bank's crest level matches the river level profile, and does not have unintentional low spots, otherwise the flow over the bank will be concentrated and the bank could be washed away.

On-line flood storage reservoirs (such as the Leigh Barrier on the Medway) rely on the operation of a control structure (often a sluice gate) to bring the storage into play. In normal circumstances, the sluice gate is open and the river passes freely on downstream. As the flood event develops, the decision is made to throttle the flow downstream by partially closing the sluice. Optimum operation requires full knowledge of the catchment hydrology and hydraulics, and preferably reasonably accurate rainfall forecasts. Operation can be greatly enhanced by the acquisition of real time rainfall and soil moisture data in the catchment, as well as flow data in the river upstream. This information can be fed into a mathematical model of the river, together with forecast data, to allow simulation of the impending flood event to facilitate operational decisions.

In designing such flood alleviation works, it is vital that a full range of flood events is examined, including those much more extreme than the 'design event'. For large raised reservoirs (capable of holding 25 000 m^3 or more, as defined in the Reservoirs Act 1975) there are prescribed rules for the

Figure 5.4. The Bourne Ditch flood storage reservoir provides flood alleviation for Windsor with no adverse impact on the environment of Windsor Great Park (photograph from the Mott MacDonald archive)

consideration of extreme floods. In other situations, designers should follow a similar practice, looking at not only extreme peak flows, but also multiple peak floods (the second peak can occur when the storage reservoir is already full), and sustained rainfall events of the sort we have recently experienced due to stationary weather systems. The design approach should explore a full range of scenarios by asking 'what if?'. In this way, any vulnerabilities in the design will be discovered and appropriate steps can be taken to address these (Figure 5.4).

likely to be successful where it is carried out upstream of a developed area and where the backing up of the water level pushes water into storage on natural flood plains within and upstream of the restored reach (e.g. the River Quaggy scheme — see Section 4.3.1).

In extreme circumstances, we should not shy away form the concept of returning riverside urban areas to the flood plain. This approach has been successfully used in North America and also in Japan, where river corridors have been cleared of housing and vital infrastructure to provide flood storage and conveyance. Clearly such an option cannot be entered into lightly but, if it presents an economically viable solution and provided that the social disbenefits can be successfully addressed, it should not be discounted. Furthermore, we should not overlook our smaller urban streams in terms of restoration potential (see Section 4.3). It is recommended that such options should be considered in cases where solutions are being sought for an urban channel flooding problem.

5.4.2 Conveyance options

Any solution that does not rely on storage can be termed a conveyance option. Traditionally this has generally meant the raising of flood defences alongside the channel to keep the flow within bank and to pass the problem on downstream (Figure 5.5). Flood diversion channels and tunnels are also considered within this category.

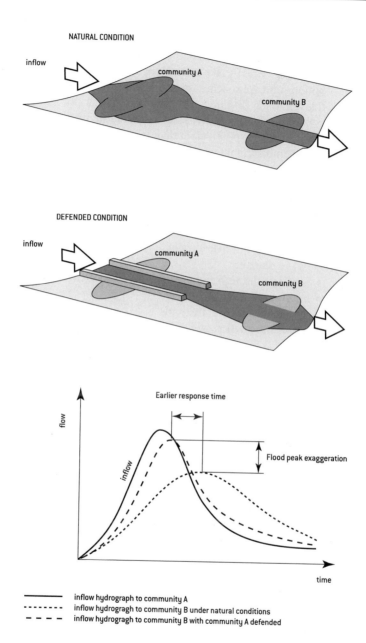

Figure 5.5. Constraining a river within higher banks simply transfers the flood problem downstream

Raised defences

Flood banks and walls will continue to form part of our front-line approach to flood risk management, but we need to explore design options and approaches to suit the increasing difficulty of justifying this approach (Figure 5.6).

Many of our raised defences are earth structures for which the integrity is less predictable than for a concrete wall. Long lengths of raised embankment were subjected to a severe test in the winter 2000 floods and there was considerable concern about the ability of the banks in question to remain safe. Research is being undertaken to help improve confidence in the performance of new and existing flood embankments. This should continue, and should include

- freeboard and overtopping
- wave damage
- seepage through and under the embankment
- reinforced soil options
- erosion protection methods
- breach formation and development.

Figure 5.6. Flood walls can blend into the urban environment. In the Autumn 2000 floods in Yorkshire, these walls at Cawood provided an effective defence against a rare flood event (photograph from the Mott MacDonald archive)

Figure 5.7. The German IBS demountable flood defence system requires a custom-built foundation and is suitable for situations where a permanent defence would destroy the amenity of the area

In some towns and cities, the construction of permanent flood defences is undesirable or impractical because of adverse impact on amenity or the lack of available space. One option is through the use of temporary or demountable flood defences. Such solutions may provide the right answer where permanent defences would destroy the local amenity, or where the risk of flooding is not sufficient to justify the cost of permanent works. This is already the subject of a DEFRA/Environment Agency research and development project (DEFRA/EA, 2001). The high level of interest generated by the 'flood defence fair' held at Bewdley in June 2001 is indicative of the potential for such systems to provide defences in situations where conventional approaches are not acceptable (Figure 5.7).

However, the applicability of temporary and demountable flood defences depends critically on the time available to deploy them. Depending on the type, size, scale and distance from storage to site, deployment can take minutes or up to half a day. Clearly, whatever time it takes must be less than the advance warning of impending flood that can be given with confidence (Figure 5.8).

Diversion channels

Like road bypass schemes, flood diversion channels tend to

- be expensive

Figure 5.8. The Californian Water Systems Aquadam™ can be deployed to protect individual properties

Figure 5.9. The Dorney Wetlands section of the recently completed Jubilee River — a major flood diversion channel for the Thames running from Maidenhead to Eton (photograph courtesy of the Environment Agency)

- be popular with the bypassed community (but not necessarily with those communities downstream)
- offer opportunities for environmental enhancement.

Such options need to be looked at carefully, with the emphasis on identifying benefits beyond flood alleviation. The diversion of the Thames at Maidenhead is not perhaps typical of such schemes, but it is a good example of a flood relief scheme being used to create environmental gain and improve the amenity of the area (Figure 5.9).

5.4.3   Other options

Flood resistant buildings

There will inevitably be occasions where development of a flood risk area will go ahead and, in these circumstances, the construction of flood resistant buildings would be appropriate. Such measures include the construction of floor levels above the predicted flood levels. Building on stilts is an obvious and often ignored approach — it is common in many other parts of the world including the United States (Mississippi Delta).

For existing buildings, solutions are likely to include

- relocating power sockets above the flood level
- using water-resistant materials for built-in furniture (e.g. kitchen units)
- replacing wooden floors with concrete
- avoiding the use of fitted carpets in downstairs rooms.

Further research into all the available options for improving the flood resistance of both existing and new buildings is required. The aim should be to identify innovative and cost-effective solutions that will be readily adopted by the building industry.

Ring dykes

In some low-lying areas, small communities can successfully be protected by encircling them with a flood embankment. This approach has been adopted in North America, and could be applicable to small villages or hamlets in low-lying parts of England and Wales. Such solutions may also be viable for individual dwellings, or farm buildings, and should not be discouraged for existing properties, even if a small loss of flood plain will result.

The appropriate design of ring dyke defences will require consideration of seepage under the surrounding embankment, as alluvial flood plains often have permeable soil strata. Such seepage becomes more of a problem in conditions of sustained high river levels, and it may be necessary to allow for the provision of a sump and pumping plant to evacuate seepage inflow from within the defended area. Seepage under the embankment can also destabilise it, especially if the retained head of water is high. Design of the embankment needs to take this risk into account.

5.5   DESIGN APPROACHES

5.5.1   Risk and uncertainty

The traditional approach to the study and design of flood alleviation works has been based on a well-tried event-based methodology. This has served flood defence engineers well for decades, but it is time for a change that recognises the inherent uncertainty in the process. The assessment of risk and the wider use of risk-based design approaches have been covered in Chapter 2, but it is worth reiterating some of the key elements as they apply to the design of flood defences in the future. These are

- looking at the performance of each scheme option across a whole range of flood events, rather than just one 'design event'
- taking account of all the levels of uncertainty in the process, and evaluating these in terms of risk in order to develop the options
- testing the robustness of the scheme design by using sensitivity tests to explore a wide range of 'what if' scenarios
- making the best use of the developing science of risk analysis and probabilistic design.

In the words of one well-informed practitioner, we need to 'take a deep breath, and jump into the probabilistic pool' in approaching flood risk management in the future. This process will be particularly important in the assessment of the impact of climate change — we can no longer rely solely upon the historic record to predict the future. However, it should be emphasised that the historic record is one of the most important sets of data that we have, and data collection should remain a high priority so that future generations can benefit from this.

Uncertainties in flood defence design

The following is a list of possible uncertainties that should be addressed in the design of any flood defence scheme. Whereas not all of these are relevant in every case, their applicability should at least be considered until it can be demonstrated that they do not apply. The list is not exhaustive.

- Accuracy of the historic record of flood levels or flood flows — be especially wary of short records (less than 20 years).
- Recent changes in the catchment upstream that may not be reflected in the data record (especially changes in land use).
- Repeated flood events during exceptionally high and prolonged periods of rainfall (e.g. autumn 2000 in parts of England and Wales).
- Impact on water levels of seasonal or longer-term changes in the river channel over time, especially siltation and weed growth.
- The accuracy of any method used to derive the flood flow at a particular site (make sure that you fully appreciate the confidence limits inherent in the method used — it is very unlikely that any estimate will be more accurate than ±10%, and it could be as bad as ±50%).
- The accuracy of any stage–discharge relationship (just because someone has plotted a graph of water level against flow does not mean that this is an accurate representation of reality — many rating curves are accurate only for low flows).
- The accuracy of any mathematical model used to predict flood levels (again, be aware of the confidence limits — do not believe any level prediction that has more than one decimal place in metres!). Errors can occur in the data input (e.g. channel cross-sections), the representation of structures (e.g. culverts), the basic mathematical relationships implicit in the model (e.g. the representation of flow in the flood plain), and the overall configuration of the model (especially a problem in complex models with multiple channels and interconnecting storage cells).

- When designing any scheme that involves flood storage, it is vital to look at a range of flood hydrographs and not just the one with the highest peak flow. A sustained low-intensity flood could result in a storage reservoir being filled unexpectedly. The chance of a second flood peak arriving after the first, and before the reservoir has had time to empty, should also be considered.
- The impact of more extreme floods than the specified design flood. This should include floods as high as the 0·1% probable flood. Consideration of how the scheme performs in such floods may lead to design changes or at least revised emergency plans.
- The failure to operate components of the scheme properly — for example, flood gates protecting individual properties not closed.
- The impact of underfunding in maintenance. Ideally, the scheme should be designed for low maintenance, but this is not always practicable. Flood embankments may settle or be worn down by cattle; budgetary constraints may lead to weed cutting once a year instead of twice.
- Blockage of culverts, trash screens, bridge arches and even open channels.
- Failure of other flood defences or components of the system, such as a drainage or sewage pumping station.
- Long-term climatic change.
- Do not be afraid to question any data or analysis, and always be prepared to ask 'what if...?'.

5.5.2 Examination of options

It has been suggested that, in the past, engineers have preselected flood defence solutions and that the option-analysis process has been little more than 'going through the motions'. Whereas this is clearly an exaggeration, it is evident that some schemes have been developed without full assessment of all options.

It is important that suitable assessment techniques are adopted to assess all options, with the unlikely contenders eliminated on reasoned grounds in the early stages to ensure that only the real options are considered in detail. This is likely to add to the cost of the study and design stages of schemes but will pay dividends in improved quality of schemes and improved confidence in them. Indeed, it is suggested that increased investment in the early stages of project development will lead to an improvement in the quality and performance of schemes.

The examination of options should consider not only their ability to withstand the 'design flood' but also consideration of their performance when overwhelmed by a more extreme flood. This will ensure that, for example, the impounding effect of flood defences, that can prolong the misery of flood victims, would be evaluated as part of the selection process and designed out where appropriate. It may also determine the choice between two otherwise equal options. Now that the *Flood Estimation Handbook* CD helps to accelerate the analysis of floods, there is no excuse for omitting the examination of far more rare floods than has been the norm during design.

In line with current practice, the range of options considered should include 'do nothing', but this should be extended in the future to include 'managed abandonment'. There can be little doubt that, in the face of the adverse impacts of climate change, the option of abandonment of a developed area will be a viable option in some circumstances.

5.5.3 Catchment flood management plans

The initiative to prepare catchment flood management plans is welcomed. However, there are several aspects of this initiative that need to be addressed to ensure that the best value is obtained. First, there has to be a balance between the need for a broad appraisal of the catchment characteristics on the one hand, and the desire to produce comprehensive catchment models on the other. The former runs the risk of devaluing the process because of the broad-brush approach, and the latter will inevitably have time and cost constraints, as well as practical limitations. These concerns should be addressed in the recently started pilot studies.

Having pointed out the risks, it is likely that considerable benefits will be achieved simply by bringing together people and organisations whose actions or interests are relevant to flood risk management in a particular catchment. Nevertheless, it would be a mistake to wait for the 'Holy Grail' of a sophisticated whole-catchment model before taking any decisions on, for example, changes to agricultural practices that would reduce flood risk.

5.5.4 Design standards

There is an inherent uncertainty in flood risk management that must be recognised in the development of solutions. Even with complex risk analysis and sophisticated probabilistic design approaches, we should not delude ourselves that we can work to millimetre accuracy. Sensitivity tests and an appreciation of the levels of uncertainty should allow engineers to make decisions on a rational and supportable basis, taking full account of climate change to the extent that can be justified by current knowledge.

In the absence of any more reliable evidence, the guidance given in *Flood and Coastal Defence Project Appraisal Guidance* (MAFF 1999d) to allow for an increase of 20% in flood flow over the first 50-year life of a typical scheme is acceptable, although further research is required to improve understanding for design. This need not necessarily mean constructing the scheme to this standard from the start. In some circumstances, particularly for major schemes, it may be prudent to allow for future enhancement of the scheme and only allow for, say, 20 years of climate change. The scheme could then be reviewed after 15 years.

There is a need for better, more reliable relationships between stage (water level) and discharge (flow). Main river flooding of infrastructure or property is generally initiated when the river water level reaches a certain value at which it overtops the river defences and spills into the flood plain. Accurate knowledge of the relationship between water level and flow at key locations in a river channel is therefore fundamental to the assessment of flood risk and the management thereof. This information is useful for the following activities

- modelling of the river hydraulics to assess flood risk and examine alternative options for mitigation
- planning and designing flood alleviation works
- operation of flood control structures

- forecasting (and subsequently issuing warnings about) rising flood levels.

Accurate stage–discharge relationships are not only required for designated flow gauging stations, but also for any significant hydraulic structure that affects the relationship between the water level and flow in the channel. This includes weirs, sluices and even bridges (Figure 5.10). An ongoing research project is examining the issue of afflux at bridges (backing up of water levels caused by the restricted waterway) with the aim of producing clear guidance (Environment Agency, 2001g).

Even at flow gauging stations, the stage–discharge relationship is often poorly understood at high flows, because many of the stations were constructed for water resources purposes and are accurate only for low to moderate flows. At more complex structures, such as the combinations of weirs and sluices often found at old mill sites, the hydraulics are particularly complex, and stage–discharge relationships often lack credibility. Inaccuracies are difficult to resolve, because

Figure 5.10. Understanding the hydraulic performance of bridges can be crucial in predicting water level in floods

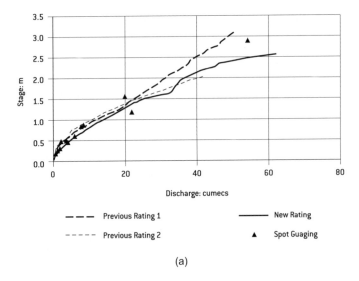

(a)

(b)

Figure 5.11. The extension and validation of rating curves for flood flows at flow gauging stations is important to ensure that we have accurate data for flood risk management: (a) rating curves from discharge measurement station; (b) flow gauging station (source Mott MacDonald)

- the sites are often inaccessible during floods
- the value of the flood flow is difficult to determine or derive.

It is therefore important that studies are undertaken to improve the accuracy of all key main river hydraulic structures, and that a programme is put in place to ensure that the ratings are regularly reviewed. Research work is being carried out in this area but more needs to be done. The impetus given to the construction of flood flow gauging stations after the Easter 1998 floods needs to be maintained to ensure that we have better data for the future (Figure 5.11).

5.5.5   Freeboard

General

'Freeboard' is the term used to describe the safety margin between the water level for which a flood defence has been designed, and the crest level of the defence. Fundamentally, it is an issue of confidence, both literally and mathematically. Literally in the sense that people would not have confidence in a defence if the water level was to rise close to overtopping. Mathematically in the sense of confidence limits, as described below.

The analysis of flood hydraulics in rivers is not a precise science, and it is important to recognise this in managing flood risk. In the design of flood defences in the past, it has been traditional to add a freeboard to the design water level based on experience and tradition. Thus, one might have added 0·3 m for a concrete wall, but 0·5 m for an earth embankment, in recognition of the latter's vulnerability to local degradation (e.g. as a result of cattle damage). Larger values may have been used where there was known to be significant wave activity that could cause overtopping.

Generally speaking, this approach is no longer acceptable. Nowadays we have more information and better tools to allow us to make more accurate and justifiable assessments of freeboard for fluvial flood defences. Full details are provided in the Environment Agency's Fluvial Freeboard Guidance Note, Technical Report W187 (Environment Agency, 2000d).

The guide sets out a logical approach to the derivation of a freeboard value for any given situation. Fundamentally, freeboard is made up of two main elements, namely uncertainties in the derivation of the flood water level, and changes that might happen in the life of the scheme.

Uncertainties

These include inaccuracies in the basic data (there may be a very short record of flood flows), inaccuracies in the hydrological analysis (flood flows may be generated from rainfall data, for example using *Flood Estimation Handbook* techniques), and inaccuracies in the mathematical model used to analyse hydraulic performance (in the mathematics, the model configuration and the assumptions made — such as channel roughness).

Also in this category are factors such as wave height and super-elevation (the raising of water level on the outside of a bend). These can be estimated using hydraulic and statistical theory, but not with absolute confidence.

Changes

Changes can be subdivided into those that we have some control over, and those that we do not. The most important one in the second category is climate change, because we cannot have any control over this as far as the short to medium term is concerned.

Those that we have some control over are listed below, together with the interventions that can help to reduce their impact

- siltation in the channel causing raised water levels (can be corrected by dredging)
- weed growth in the channel (this is a seasonal phenomenon that can be dealt with by regular weed clearance)
- settlement or degradation of the flood defence (regular inspection and maintenance will correct this).

However, in considering the above, it is vitally important to appreciate that the interventions are *intermittent*, and that there will therefore be a build up in the problem before it is resolved. If the design has been based on a smooth earth channel with no siltation, then higher than predicted water levels will be achieved in advance of the dredging and weed clearance operations. These need to be allowed for in the design.

Risk

The assessment of risk is fundamental to the process of designing flood defences, not least in the calculation of an appropriate freeboard. It is important to consider the consequences of overtopping of flood defences as well as the likelihood thereof.

Furthermore, it is important to examine the consequences of more extreme floods than the design flood, to ensure that the performance of the defences in such conditions does not place the defended community at even greater risk than if there had been no defences at all. Or if it does, to be aware of this so that appropriate plans can be put in place to mitigate that risk.

5.6 POLICY FOR EXISTING DEFENDED AREAS IN OUR TOWNS AND CITIES

In England, national planning policy guidance on development in areas at risk from flooding has recently been revised and updated in *Planning Policy Guidance Note 25, Development and Flood Risk* (DTLR, 2001). The new guidance adopts a risk-based sequential approach to planning decisions, giving priority to development in areas of lower flood risk.

However, for existing towns and cities on flood plains, there will generally be a strong justification for continuing to provide a high standard of flood defence. In addition, notwithstanding the stricter controls in *Planning Policy Guidance Note 25*, there will still be some justifiable development on flood plains. This could be, for example

- where there is a low to medium risk (less than a 100–1 chance of a flood in any year)
- where there is an area of brownfield land within a defended area that is otherwise ideal for development
- where a defended area can be extended to facilitate a major new development, subject to a satisfactory and comprehensive flood risk assessment, and with the proviso that the developer would fund any new defences and/or the upgrading of existing defences.

Nevertheless, the presence of existing flood defences will not preclude the making of some strategic decisions, such as relocating essential civil infrastructure, including schools and hospitals, away from flood risk areas when the time comes for major refurbishment or redevelopment.

It has been suggested that 'flood defences give a false sense of security' because they can never give protection against all flood events. This is a reaction to the recent floods and is a bit like saying seat belts give a false sense of security, or travelling by train gives a false sense of security. Many defences are designed to provide protection for fairly rare events (as are seat belts) and therefore do provide a high degree of, but not absolute, security. Accordingly, it is important to raise general awareness of the vulnerability to potential flooding and to develop an understanding of the situation without causing unnecessary alarm.

Furthermore, the discouragement of any development in defended areas needs careful consideration, as the alternative may be less desirable. Of course, in areas where it is clear that the present defences are inadequate and/or unsuitable, then development should be discouraged. If the defences can be sustained, then encouraging more development within the defended area could generate funds (from developers) to help to provide and maintain appropriate defences.

Whatever is decided in any particular location, it is clearly important that the decision-making process is backed up by a full assessment of the risks and benefits, making use of the latest technology in mathematical modelling and risk analysis.

5.7   OPERATION AND MAINTENANCE

5.7.1   Flood defence assets

The replacement value of fluvial flood defence infrastructure in England and Wales is estimated at around £5·5 billion. This figure has been derived from Table 3.3c of the DEFRA report *National Appraisal of Assets at Risk from Flooding and Coastal Erosion* (DEFRA, 2001), taking the annual cost of replacement £86·78 million and multiplying it by an estimated 60-year life, and increasing the figure to allow for flood defences in Wales. The equivalent figure for all flood defence and coastal protection infrastructure is around £16 billion.

The current annual investment in maintenance of all these assets is around £80 million, approximately 0·5% of the replacement cost. This is considered to be the minimum level of investment to maintain defences in a safe condition. Such a level of investment will almost inevitably lead to the gradual decline in the state of the flood defence infrastructure. This appears to be borne out by the recently published National Audit Office report which indicated that some 40% of the defences are in fair, poor or very poor condition (National Audit Office, 2001).

Although the basis for the assessment of the condition of flood defences can be questioned, in terms of the validity and accuracy of the methods used, there is clearly cause for concern. Urgent consideration should therefore be given to increased levels of expenditure on asset maintenance — perhaps as much as double the present level of investment.

The current situation with flood defence assets can perhaps be compared with the nation's waterways. At the end of March 2000, British Waterways was facing a backlog of maintenance arrears valued at £237 million (British Waterways, 2001). They are now steadily tackling this, but it will take a long time to catch up (it will not be completed until 2021). It is by no means clear to what extent a similar backlog applies to flood defences — clearly it is important to find out and face up to it.

5.7.2   Flood defence asset surveys

Maintenance is, by its nature, a planned and programmed activity. It relies on a full knowledge of the systems to be maintained, including the original design and construction, as well as the current condition. Although the Environment Agency has taken steps to ensure that an accurate asset register is in place, more work is required to ensure that this is

- in a form that facilitates planning and programming maintenance activities
- kept up to date
- consistent across England and Wales.

This need is already recognised in DEFRA's *High Level Targets for Flood and Coastal Defence* (MAFF, 1999b), namely

Target 1
Each operating authority to prepare a publicly available policy statement on coastal and flood defence, should allow identification of 'critical ordinary watercourses' and the action proposed to alleviate flood risk from them.

Target 4
The Environment Agency (in partnership with other operating authorities) is required to develop a national database on all flood and coastal defence assets, regardless of which operating authority is responsible for them, and including those in private ownership.

Target 5
The Environment Agency is to ensure that there is a programme of regular inspection of flood defences on main rivers and critical ordinary watercourses.

With regard to Target 4, it is understood that an interim database is in operation, pending development of a new database. However, the provision of information for the database has been 'patchy'. This requires a renewed effort to get the new database fully operational and populated with valid and up-to-date data.

For Target 5, it is reported that programmes are in place for inspecting main river defences but it is proving difficult to get the cooperation of operating authorities for ordinary watercourses. This is an unfortunate situation, especially since a significant proportion of the flooding in the autumn of 2000 came from non-main river sources. Critical ordinary watercourses will encompass many urban watercourses but it is unclear whether or not all channels that pose a significant risk have been properly identified as critical.

The establishment of an accurate and reliable database of all flood defence infrastructure, regardless of ownership, is vital for the operation, maintenance, and eventual replacement of this infrastructure. Preferably this should be placed in the public domain.

In the case of riparian ownership, any responsibility for drainage maintenance should be added to registered land titles. This would most readily be achieved at re-registration of a land transfer. In addition, all surveys for future property sales should include an indication of likely flood risk.

5.7.3 Operation of flood defences

Most flood defences are 'static' engineering structures that require little in the way of operation — they simply stand and resist the flood when called upon to do so. However, there are structures that require active operation to ensure that the flood risk is managed as efficiently and effectively as possible. Sluice gates and pumping stations are two obvious examples, both of which can be set to operate automatically in response to a rising (or falling) water level (Figure 5.12). Accurate predictions of rainfall and runoff across a catchment, in terms of areal extent, timing and quantity would therefore help to optimise the operation of such flood defences. Poor predictions cause problems in that structures may be operated sub-optimally, leading to, for example, premature filling of a storage reservoir. There is therefore a clear need to improve the accuracy of rainfall and runoff forecasting, not only to allow more effective operation of flood defence

Figure 5.12. Effective operation and maintenance of complex flood defence infrastructure relies on detailed knowledge of the condition of the defences, as well as full understanding of their hydraulic performance (photograph of Colwick Sluice on the River Trent, from the Mott MacDonald archive)

infrastructure, but also to allow the issue of more accurate and timely flood warnings.

The extent to which this is achievable remains in doubt. In reality, the predictive accuracy is within the margin of error associated with assigning a rainfall to a catchment based on recorded rainfall from a few rain gauges. In other words, without additional telemetered gauges, it will be difficult to improve significantly the accuracy of rainfall predictions. However, some improvement in rainfall quantity forecasts can be expected over the next five to ten years. Software systems can be put in place to aid flood forecasters, but there will continue to be a reliance on local knowledge and experience in the operation of key flood defence infrastructure.

Experience in Italy, the United States and the Netherlands indicates that telemetered hydro-meteorological methods can be used effectively to reduce flood impact.

5.7.4 Maintenance of flood defences

Part of the problem experienced with the maintenance of flood defences stems from the fact that, in the past, there has been a tendency to 'think in boxes'. In particular, the design and construction of new flood defences has been quite distinct from the operation and maintenance of those defences. Whereas it would be untrue to say that there has been no link between the two activities in the past, it is apparent that there is a strong case for better integration in the future.

There have been cases where the design of a scheme has been based on reasonable assumptions regarding the hydraulic roughness of a channel but these assumptions have never been translated into an appropriate maintenance programme. As a result, vegetation has perhaps been cleared infrequently and irregularly, whereas a much more systematic cutting programme would be required to achieve the design hydraulic performance. Such incompatibility might, of course, not be exposed until a flood arrives.

Many of the existing flood defences are earth flood embankments that have been constructed over many decades. Our understanding of how these perform in extreme floods, and what is the appropriate maintenance regime, are incomplete. The frequency of inspection of defences should be related to the level of risk. The management of earth flood defences needs to be taken more seriously, especially where they are intended to act as overtopped weirs for part of the flood event.

5.8   FLOOD DEFENCE EXPENDITURE

The recent MAFF report *National Appraisal of Assets at Risk from Flooding and Coastal Erosion in England and Wales* (MAFF, 2000) makes a clear recommendation that capital investment in flood defence infrastructure should increase by at least 100%. In parallel with this increase, there would have to be a commensurate increase in expenditure on operation and maintenance, as well as sustained investment on flood forecasting and warning.

5.9   RESEARCH AND DEVELOPMENT

Some view 'research' as any investigation with a 'blue skies' opportunity to explore lateral thinking and novel ideas. By contrast, 'consulting' may well have tightly drawn terms of reference with specific deliverables. For the purposes of this book, we commend both forms of contracting to improve the national capability to manage flood risk. Simply for convenience we have brought recommendations for both types of work into this one section.

The thematic programme of research and development recently established by MAFF and the Environment Agency (MAFF/EA, 2000) is already beginning to yield positive results in terms of a focus on the end user, combined with the bringing together of a wide range of parties interested in each particular study area. The issues of risk and uncertainty are key elements of many of the topics under the engineering theme, and they are also fundamental to the risk evaluation and uncertainty theme, as well as being of relevance to the broad-scale modelling theme. Interaction between the themes therefore adds value to the process without detracting from the focus of any particular project within a theme.

The concerted action programmes, such as that on operation and maintenance (engineering theme) are strongly supported as a means of further developing particular topic areas. One of the key benefits of these is the bringing together of interested parties and the avoidance of 'thinking in boxes'.

However, there has been a decline in the investment in research and development so far this year, partly as a result of the change in approach and the time taken to establish the themes. The level of investment in the DEFRA/Environment Agency research and development programme should be built up to the figure established in the Penning-Rowsell Report (MAFF, 1999c) and maintained at that level, at least until the next review (namely £5·2 million each year).

The development of 'partnering' relationships with leading research and model development organisations in the UK is welcomed (e.g. HR Wallingford and the Centre for Ecology and Hydrology). Such relationships, if managed properly, will not preclude the use of other organisations, but will facilitate the development of priority projects and avoid wasted effort. Involvement of model developers in partnering relationships should speed up the delivery of research and development results to practitioners and allow the often contentious issues of intellectual property rights and exploitation rights to be dealt with in a global manner rather than the ad hoc arrangements that are often made on

Figure 5.13. Building flood defences will continue to be one of our key strategies for flood risk management, but we cannot go on building ever higher walls. The ongoing research and development programme will help us to better understand the risks, and to develop new responses (photograph from the Mott MacDonald archive)

individual commissions. In the same vein, DEFRA/Environment Agency should not shy away from the direct appointment of teams where this can clearly be justified. This approach is particularly appropriate in the case of small commissions. The majority of research and development work should, however, continue to be bid competitively, with the budget identified in advance, and selection made on the basis of the quality of the team that will work on the project.

Whereas it will always be appropriate to rely on some voluntary (unpaid) contributions from academia and industry, there should be an increased recognition of the value of such contributions, and more willingness to pay for them (Figure 5.13).

There should continue to be an emphasis on the end user, and on the process of ensuring that the latest techniques are readily available to practitioners. On the particular topic of risk, the Penning-Rowsell report envisaged 'a structured programme of training courses held at various locations throughout the UK and designed to attract a wide range of practitioners'. We believe that this approach should be adopted wherever there is a need to spread the word on the latest design approaches, and it would be appropriate for such activities to be subsidised, if not funded, from the research and development budget.

6 Flood management tools

Stephen Huntingdon, Donald Knight and Kenneth MacDougall

6.1 EXISTING SYSTEMS

The Environment Agency's recently published long-term vision for the environment was grouped under nine themes. The long-term objective with respect to flood risk is stated thus (Environment Agency, 2001e)

> Flood warnings and sustainable defences will continue to prevent deaths from flooding. Property damage and distress will be minimised. The role of wetlands in reducing flood risks will be recognised and all environmental benefits from natural floods will be maximised.

The supporting document says little about the methodologies required to fulfil this objective. However, Section 3.1 has outlined the basis of catchment flood management plans, Chapters 4 and 5 the engineering issues, and Section 3.2 the background to some of the modelling tools and systems currently available. The specific tools for flood management are now considered in further detail.

6.2 FLOOD FREQUENCY ESTIMATION

Flood studies regularly require the estimation of the peak discharge for a flood with a probable annual chance of occurrence, $n-1$ chance flood, where n years is substantially longer than the available record (as discussed in Chapters 1 and 2).

In a recent report (Bayliss and Reed, 2001), the distribution method advocated is the same as that in the *Flood Estimation*

Handbook (CEHW, 1999), namely use of the (three parameter) generalised logistic distribution for pooled analysis of UK annual maximum series, but a graphical approach when reconciling such estimates with historical flood data. The flood peak (m^3s^{-1}) is plotted against the logistic reduced-variate, y, where $y = ln\{p_i/(1 - p_i)\}$ and p_i is the exceedance probability. The reduced variate scale transforms frequency to a linear axis and separate equations are presented for historical and systematic data. These are given as

$$p_i = \left(\frac{i - \alpha}{k + 1 - 2\alpha}\right)\left(\frac{k}{n}\right), i = 1...k$$

$$p_i = \frac{k}{n} + \left(\frac{n - k}{n}\right)\left(\frac{i - k - \alpha}{s - e + 1 - 2\alpha}\right), i = k + 1...k + s - e$$

in which $\alpha = 0.44$, consistent with the Gringorten formula, n is the combined record length (in years) of the historical and systematic data, i.e. $n = h + s$, k is the total number of extreme floods (i.e. the number of floods exceeding the threshold flow value, x_0) in the combined period, i.e. $k = e + e'$, where e is the number of systematic extreme floods larger than x_0 and e' is the number of historic extreme floods larger than x_0. Note e or e' can be zero. See Reed (1999) and Robson and Reed (1999) for details of the *Flood Estimation Handbook* approach.

Webster (1998) found, using a continuous rainfall–runoff model, that the annual maximum floods of a given return period result in storms with a lesser return period, falling on wetter catchments than assumed in the *Flood Studies Report* (NERC, 1975). The characteristics of observed floods in 210 UK catchments were compared with the design guidelines in the *Flood Studies Report* and the *Flood Estimation Handbook* by Webster and Ashfaq (2001). In general terms, it was found that the observed maxima had a higher catchment wetness index (CWI) and a higher range of percentage runoff (PR) then the design events. It is important that the strengths and limitations of the *Flood Estimation Handbook* should be reassessed periodically, in the light of study and knowledge gained through applying it within the UK. New flood data related to extreme meteorological events, and the links between flow and water level, should be incorporated into the *Flood Estimation Handbook*, and the proposed *Flood Plain Handbook*, to improve their methodology and to test their underlying assumptions.

The *Flood Estimation Handbook* (CEHW, 1999) should be used to explore the sensitivity of the flood regime to climate change and land use. It is also important that the strengths and limitations of the handbook are reassessed periodically, in the light of study and knowledge gained through applying it within the UK. New flood data related to extreme meteorological events, and the links between flow and water level, should be incorporated in both the *Flood Estimation Handbook* and the proposed *Flood Plain Handbook* to improve their methodology and to test their underlying assumptions.

Over-reliance should not be placed on wholly statistical analysis of past records for estimating extreme flow or level values and worst case flood scenarios should be examined using coupled models with degrees of uncertainty attached. There is therefore a need to develop and integrate further the hydrodynamic modelling of channel change and sedimentation with hydrological sensitivity analyses to improve the accuracy of flood level estimates. This model coupling should occur at catchment and sub-catchment scales, and there is also a need to pool best use in their practice.

The value of modelling flood phenomena in this way and at such a scale is that, unlike reliance on purely historic data, extreme events may be simulated in order to

- test 'what if' scenarios
- examine rainfall and floods larger than ever experienced
- study changes in land use
- assess the impact of engineered solutions on reducing flood risk.

An analogy might be drawn from the aeronautical field in which the test pilot is the equivalent of the model developer, testing software to discover its ultimate envelope, and the commercial pilot is the equivalent of the flood defence engineer, who is trained in the interests of safety to respond to numerous events in such a way that they can all be competently dealt with.

6.3   FLOOD FORECASTING

The Environment Agency's National Flood Warning Centre seeks to improve the quality of the flood warning service it provides to the public by coordinating efforts within the Environment Agency. The actual forecasts and warnings are undertaken at a regional level, commensurate with local models and knowledge. In a review of good practice in flood forecasting and warning (Mott MacDonald, 2000), differences were noted between Environment Agency regions for the following key activities

- event management (responsibilities, liaison arrangements between regions, office layout for effective crisis management and staffing, event recording and documentation)
- detection, by way of incoming data and monitoring (weather forecasts and tidal/coastal forecasts)
- rainfall radar, antecedent conditions (rain and level/flow gauges, telemetry and monitoring)
- forecasting of fluvial floods (types of rainfall–runoff model and use of models)
- warnings (procedures, automatic voice messaging, use of media, *Floodline* and other methods) and response
- post-event data collection and archiving.

This review, together with Dent (2001), provide a valuable snapshot of some of the issues in flood warning and also indicate the seriousness with which the Environment Agency takes its responsibilities with regard to both flood forecasting and warning.

Since the issue of Mott MacDonald's draft report in September 2000, the Environment Agency has moved to minimise the difference between regions. The final report (under preparation at the time of writing) shows the Environment Agency adopting more standard procedures through the introduction of new technology and the internal dissemination of good practice.

The aim of the National Flood Warning Centre to be world leading is to be applauded. However, it is not apparent how it can achieve this objective at the flood forecasting end of its responsibilities unless it recruits (and retains) internationally known experts in this precise field. There appears to be considerable scope for improving flood forecasts through improved modelling capabilities. As pointed out by Mott MacDonald (2000), this is especially so for fast-response catchments and for exceptional circumstances, such as dam break, embankment breaching and reservoir overtopping.

Ways of integrating knowledge between the disciplines of hydrology and hydraulics are required for effective flood risk management. Impetus should be given to the establishment of a good database of flood events. This should include the provision of additional flood flow measuring stations, and the development of reliable stage–discharge relationships for all existing stations and key hydraulic structures. It is suggested that as a first step stage–discharge data and rating curves at all gauging locations should be added to the *Flood Estimation Handbook* (CEHW, 1999), as it is common to both disciplines.

It is instructive to note that there is no agreed national standard with regard to models, although some regions have 'adequate' rainfall–runoff component models.

It is suggested that over reliance should not be placed on wholly statistical analysis of past records for estimating extreme flow or level values, but that 'worst case' flood scenarios should be tested with coupled models with degrees of uncertainty attached. There is therefore a need to develop both hydrological and hydrodynamic models together at catchment and sub-catchment scales, and also a need to pool best use in their practice. The value of modelling flood phenomena in this way, and at such a scale, is that unlike reliance on purely historic data, extreme events may be simulated in order to test 'what if' scenarios, to examine rainfall and floods larger than ever experienced, to study changes in land use and to assess the impact of engineered solutions on reducing flood risk. An analogy might be drawn from the aeronautical field in which the 'test pilot' is the equivalent of the 'model developer', testing software to discover its ultimate envelope, and the 'commercial pilot' is the equivalent of the 'flood defence engineer', who is trained in the interests of safety to respond to numerous 'events' in such a way that they can all be dealt with competently.

6.4   FLOOD RISK MAPPING

6.4.1   *Background*

Historic floods produce the best flood plain records (levels and extent) and are extremely valuable in indicating flood risk areas, assuming the actual discharge and flow frequency are known. Modelling, although vital, is not a panacea. The recent publication of flood risk maps by the Environment Agency, based on modelling projections, has had a huge benefit in terms of raising public awareness. If people who live in a flood risk area are aware of the risk, they are much more likely to be receptive to flood warnings and be more inclined to protect themselves and their property (e.g. by simple flood proofing measures) (Figure 6.1).

The history of mapping the outline of a flooded area goes back further than most people realise, a good example being the marked-up map for Derby for a Derbyshire Derwent flood of 1875, held by the Derbyshire County Council archives. Unfortunately, no systematic approach ever caught on in other major cities. Most planning authorities were left until recently with River Board maps of the flooded areas in March 1947, which was considered the highest known flood in many areas. Additional flood outlines were added as the years went by, but the system remained one of hard-copy maps that few people knew existed.

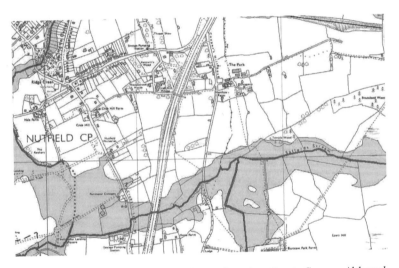

Figure 6.1. A section of a flood risk map for a location in Surrey. Although providing valuable information in an easy to understand format, there is a real danger that people located outside the 100:1 chance line will believe they are not at risk from flooding

6.4.2   Recent developments

Insurers, from the 1990s onwards, have taken a keen interest in national-scale mapping of environmental hazards. The Glasgow floods in 1994 prompted one firm to visit local government offices to capture digitally the outline of the flooded areas. Similar efforts have been made subsequently by specialist firms servicing the insurance industry with perils software, however these remain in-house datasets.

The Environment Agency was spurred by the Easter 1998 floods through Stratford, Evesham, Northampton, Banbury and Kidlington to employ consultants to create the Flood Plain Explorer CD versions. Eight CDs cover England and Wales, with snapshots of local flood plains being available on the web. The best information was sought for the 100–1 chance flood plain extent (1% annual probability of flooding or 100-year return period). Priority was given to the calibrated model results from the flood extent mapping programme that came out of the Water Resources Act 1991, second place was given to the flood of record from the Environment Agency, and the Institute of Hydrology digital terrain model (IHDTM) flood map was used to in-fill where other knowledge was absent. Detail was also available for tidal flood risk areas from a national study by Halcrow for the former National Rivers Authority.

The largest outline of those available was used for the first version issued in the autumn of 1999. A slightly revised version was issued in 2000, and the Environment Agency is committed to its continual improvement. It hopes to incorporate far more information from its lidar (light detection and ranging) surveys in future. This ongoing government-led initiative to produce flood risk maps for the whole of England and Wales is supported. Even though many of the current flood plain maps are approximate, or in need of revision for local flood plain building changes, they have already done a great deal to improve awareness of flood risk, and to guide planning authorities in development control.

6.4.3   Future development

There is a pressing need to update flood risk maps and to improve their accuracy, especially in development 'hot spots'. This work should be carried out by the Environment Agency and not left to individual developers that are only interested in particular sites. It is important that the maps are based on sound science and kept up to date. The full corpus of Ordnance Survey level data should be incorporated, or one arm of government and the community is prevented from gaining value from the work of another arm of government.

Measures should be put in place to ensure that, where individual studies are commissioned, the results are made available to the Environment Agency so that they can be taken into consideration in the updating of the flood risk maps. As the quality and accuracy of the flood risk maps is improved, consideration should be given to 'zoning', whereby areas are classified in terms of the risk of flooding rather than the current simplistic 'in or out' approach to the natural flood plain. Initially, this extra map detail might indicate merely that either urban or agricultural defence levels apply to a reach.

There should also be free access to more detailed information that will allow people to make their own informed judgements about flood risk. This could include, for example, records of flood levels reached in any given (postcoded) street. The Environment Agency retains records of many flood peak levels in urban and rural areas but the records are underused as they remain unpublished.

With this in mind, it is important that more effort is made during and immediately after a flood to gather information of flood levels, sources of runoff, direction and speed of flow. Such activities will clearly put a strain on already overloaded Environment Agency and local authority staff, so it would be wise to set up arrangements that allow the calling in of consultants and survey companies to gather the information required. The extent of information to be acquired could be enhanced by encouraging local people to record peak levels and timings. Funds should be available to support these activities when they are required.

6.5   FLOW FORECASTING AND REAL TIME CONTROL

Data and information will be at the heart of any flow forecasting system and are likely to be used increasingly in a multi-functional way. 'The real time environmental data is increasingly being integrated to service the needs of several users (e.g. river flow and catchment conditions are required within the Environment Agency for flood warning, water quality and resource management, fisheries, navigation and environmental protection specialists' (Haywood, 2001). It is perceived that 'This is to be delivered by a telemetry service, either provided by one distributed, resilient system, or by two similar systems (e.g. North and South) capable of completely backing each other up' (Haywood, 2001).

Given the increased use of data, the greater requirement of models for data and the more stringent calibration requirements of models, there should be steps taken to ensure a sufficient number of weather radar, rainfall and river water level gauges, soil moisture instruments, as well as continual improvement to the many flow gauging sites (weirs, flumes and gauging stations). There is an urgent need to modernise the oldest parts of the various regional Environment Agency telemetry systems to take in a denser network of sensors. This need has now been recognised by the Environment Agency, and a programme of updating is now underway. One priority is an improved display system for readings so that rapid unambiguous messages are available to relatively inexperienced staff as well as those familiar with the quirks of existing technology. Regular data collection should also include monitoring parameters related to geotechnical and structural checks on flood defences. The frequency of inspection of defences should be related to the level of risk.

Flood forecasting modelling systems (FFMS) operate in real time and are based on different types of model and are at various stages of development.

Real time river flow forecasting is technically demanding, as is the updating of a forecast based typically on

(a) an inadequately structured model
(b) poor estimation of model parameters, and
(c) data errors of a systematic or random nature.

The errors between the simulated and the observed discharge hydrograph can be categorised as being of three types, namely volume (amplitude) errors, phase errors and shape errors (Becker and Serban, 1990).

Unlike the off-line design mode use of models, which only requires an appropriate rainfall–runoff model and a suitable hydrodynamic model, real-time forecasting requires a third and additional type of model, a robust and technologically advanced updating procedure or model. There are thus three components in a real-time forecasting system

- *rainfall–runoff model* for flow magnitude (quasi-physically based)
- *hydrodynamic model* for flood levels (one-dimensional, two-dimensional and three-dimensional versions)
- *updating model* for use in real time (algorithm based).

Depending on how the updating procedure is applied (manual or automatic), rules are required, as indicated by Serban and Askew (1991). Different techniques are required depending on whether storage content updating, parameter updating, input updating and output updating is used. Each has its own particular philosophy.

The main rationale of adjusting the water content of the various storage elements of the model is that errors in the input variables of the model are accumulated and appear as errors in the water content of the model. Thus, if these water contents are modified in accordance with the observed discrepancy between the model simulated discharge and the observed discharge then a better discharge forecast may be obtained. A critique of the use of the Kalman filter in the context of real-time hydrological forecasting has been summed up thus: 'Despite the mathematical elegance and the flexibility of the Kalman filter, its application in the hydrological context is associated with many practical problems and theoretical flaws' (Shamseldin, 1996).

Parameter updating involves adjustments of the various values of the parameters in the model at each time step, but is not inappropriate for real-time forecasting. Of more use is input updating, which is normally carried out on a trial and error basis, arising from the fact that many rainfall–runoff models have complex structures that prohibit the model input being expressed as an explicit function of the model outputs. Output updating does not interfere with the internal operation of the simulation model, and may be applied in two ways, one based on error prediction and the other is based on the use of a linear transfer function (LTF). A number of real-time forecasting models are based on the former, for example the autoregressive (AR) models and the autoregressive moving average (ARMA) models. The application of AR, ARMA and LTFM to the SMAR simple lumped conceptual rainfall–evaporation–runoff model is discussed fully by Shamseldin (1996).

Other notable contributions to the debate on real-time forecasting are those by Moore (1999) and Refsgaard (1997). Moore (1999) reviews three models, the Severn–Trent conceptual model, based on the Institute of Hydrology conceptual model (IHCM), the Thames region conceptual model and the probability distributed model (PDM). Updating of the forecast is by a range of procedures. Refsgaard (1997) likewise reviews conceptual models, but provides a framework for classifying updating procedures. State variable updating is found to be more reliable than error prediction when time delays (i.e. longer river channels) do not dominate. A common problem experienced by most, if not all, of the updating routines is the problem of distinguishing between phase and amplitude errors. The use of the Kalman filter is advocated in connection with the assimilation of remote sensing data, which may well be corrupted by significant noise. The use of the filter in updating spatial remote sensing data non linearities in measurement and system equations is not recommended.

Other developments in river flow forecasting are based on 'pattern recognition', the 'nearest neighbour' approach and the use of the neural network technique (Shamseldin *et al.*, 2001).

Real-time river flow forecasting is technically demanding, as is the updating of a forecast, which is based typically on

- inadequately structured model
- poor estimation of model parameters
- data errors of a systematic or random nature.

The errors between the simulated and the observed discharge hydrograph can be categorised as being of three types (Becker and Serban, 1990), namely

- volume (amplitude) errors
- phase errors
- shape errors.

It is noteworthy that in the Environment Agency's autumn 2000 *Floods Review Regional Reports*, the flow forecasting performance graphs and data were presented exclusively in terms of peak water level and phase.

The state of the Environment Agency's 'River flow forecasting systems' (RFFS) (Mott MacDonald, 2000) presents a disturbing picture of its capability in river-level forecasting. There are very large variations in methodology between the eight regions, ranging from use of 'judgement' and 'trigger levels' to 'models', some used for 15 years but currently in need of an upgrade. Again the difference between flow forecasting and level forecasting is apparent.

Less attention often appears to be paid to the updating procedures for river flow forecasting systems compared with the development of model structures for rainfall–runoff models. This balance needs to be redressed if good real-time control is aspired to.

The most striking comment made by the National Flood Warning Centre was that no flood warning has yet been given to the public solely on the basis of running a rainfall–runoff algorithm. This suggests that either

- it is possible to run the Environment Agency service solely by flood level monitoring
- that there is a lack of confidence in a 'thin' network of sensors and their subsequent calibration
- that the uncertainties involved cannot be adequately assessed.

Dent (2001) lists a number of issues (e.g. quantitative precipitation forecasts, radar accuracy, the use and value of radar, telemetry systems, catchment wetness index monitoring, use of models, levels of staffing and lack of experience/knowledge) that impinge on operational effectiveness.

Flood hydrograph forecasting is not yet being trusted by those who use it in flood emergencies in this country. Current methodologies should be continually refined so that state-updating from catchment sensors is employed in forecasting models to the maximum extent that brings useful performance gains.

The development of regional flood response models should be progressed more urgently. Although complete standardisation may be unhelpful in all cases, core concepts and algorithms should be transparent enough to perceive why differences are needed.

Consideration should be given to moving to risk-based forecasting and production of risk-based forecast products for both internal use by flood warning officers and external dissemination. Confidence in forecasts has been raised as an important issue and, whereas the Environment Agency continues to forecast only absolute peaks and threshold crossings, the potential for inaccuracy is high. Errors in forecasts propagate from

- sparse and unrepresentative monitoring networks
- measurement errors

- missing values
- inappropriate model formulation
- inappropriate model calibration.

Updating and error prediction can improve forecasts considerably but there is still uncertainty about what confidence can be placed on the modified forecast.

Flood warning services using Teletext/Ceefax or the internet remain disappointing, for example Ceefax page 419 for flood warnings typically gives merely the number of warnings in force for each Environment Agency region. It rarely names the tributary and never the communities that may be affected. As a device it is as useless as meteorological forecasts that warn of 'localised flooding in Northern England'. No damage reduction is ever likely to occur without more precision. The engineering profession can deliver more appropriate technology (as real-time in-car navigation systems are beginning to show), but the insurance industry needs to show more financial commitment to loss avoidance by modern techniques.

It can be anticipated that internet and text messaging technology will lead very soon to the development of local skilled 'amateur' flood forecasting activities. Thus, the public, as with weather forecasts, will have to deal with rival messages on different channels. Certain types of message may be useful to particular groups, for example a service to alert drivers may be provided by the message 'road flooded ahead to x centimetres depth'.

6.6   AVAILABILITY OF DATA

The National Flood Warning Centre is committed to giving the public full and adequate warning concerning floods. The centre's public awareness campaign, including the new 'floodwatch' terminology and *Floodline*, which coincided with the autumn 2000 floods, received good media coverage at just the right time. The flood risk maps have also begun the process of educating the public about having to learn to live with rivers and the reality of the risk arising from floods. The question then follows as to how much information should be made available, either in terms of raw data or processed information.

With greater access to the internet and familiarity with information-searching systems, the appetite by some sections of the public for relevant information will increase. It would assist the development of an educated public if core hydrometric data (e.g. rainfall figures, runoff rates, water level and stage–discharge data) were available at key sites. The Environment Agency's hydrometric section, duly funded, could provide an environmental service of significance, somewhat akin to the Meteorological Office, publishing a daily digest on the internet. In the same way, the Centre for Ecology and Hydrology's monthly digest should be freely available. The more detailed information collected and processed by the hydrometric service of the Environment Agency should find its way more readily into the public domain through a series of reports or internet-based information, akin to that produced by the US Geological Survey. The great strength of the US Geological Survey is that it is a publicly funded service. From December 2001, flood warnings are now available on the Environment Agency's website. These flood warnings are available for 1300 Local Flood Warning Areas, updated every 15 minutes and the user can search by postcode, town or river. The site is designed to take up to a million hits a day and will significantly increase the public's access to flood warning information.

6.7 FUTURE TOOLS AND PROCEDURES/SYSTEMS FOR FLOOD MANAGEMENT

Given the episodic nature of floods and the need for intensive forecasting and crisis management, use could be made of staff in hydrometric and modelling teams to develop and continually upgrade the calibration of models and to test them on a range of 'what if' scenarios.

The benefits of undertaking all the section 105 (Water Resources Act 1991) survey work should now be realised as a driver in the better use of hydrodynamic models in both design and real-time forecasting. There is a need to develop robust river flow forecasting models across all regions of the Environment Agency. There is a need to replace obsolete hardware and software.

Greater collaboration between all parties (e.g. research institutes, academics, practitioners, software vendors and the Environment Agency) is required if real progress is to be made in this technically demanding area. The UK has an excellent record in developing tools for flood management but perhaps less success in promoting and marketing these skills overseas, particularly compared to say Delft in the Netherlands and the Danish Hydraulics Institute (DHI) in Denmark.

6.8   RESEARCH AND DEVELOPMENT REQUIREMENTS

The Research Council research and development programmes in a number of areas should be brought to bear more urgently on flooding issues, given its national importance. The excellent work undertaken by the Natural Environment Research Council (NERC) on the *Flood Estimation Handbook* (CEHW, 1999) and that by the Engineering and Physical Sciences Research Council (EPSRC) on the flood channel facility typifies what can be achieved through long-term funded research at a strategic level. There is, however, continuing disappointment in the community over the continuing division between hydrological-based science, loosely associated with NERC, and engineering-based science, loosely associated with EPSRC. The engineering-based and science-based dichotomy is unhelpful and is particularly inappropriate when studying fluvial processes.

NERC and EPSRC should link more closely on fluvial issues, both in terms of fieldwork and development of models. There appears to be a greater awareness of this at a European level, with considerable collaboration across national boundaries than between UK research councils. Progress is only likely to be made by integration of the core 'science' in fluvial processes and in relating models across the many disciplines involved, not necessarily in a structural way, but through an understanding of the fundamental concepts.

6.9   EMERGENCY PLANNING

Emergency planning is coordinated by the local authorities in cooperation with the emergency services, Environment Agency, utility companies and the voluntary sector. National policy on emergency planning is the responsibility of the Cabinet Office in England (which took over from the Home Office in June 2001) and the National Assembly in Wales. A national review is underway (Cabinet Office, 2001), partly prompted by the autumn 2000 floods, which will cover all aspects of the way civil emergencies are handled across the country.

Work is carried out at three levels.

- *Emergency planning and exercising* — preparation and regular review of emergency plans to deal with civil emergencies at the county and local level, together with inter-agency exercises to test their effectiveness. Such plans may be generic or directed to particular threats, such as flooding. Many towns and villages at risk from flooding do not yet have specific flood emergency plans.
- *Emergency response* — major incidents require the special mobilisation and organisation of many agencies. Initially the police coordinate the activities of all those responding to an incident, through inter-agency 'gold' and 'silver' command and control structures, although each agency exercises control over their own specific area of responsibility (see Section 10.1.1).
- *Recovery* — when an emergency situation has stabilised, and the requirement moves to coordination of recovery measures, the police will normally hand over coordination to the local authorities.

The feedback on the autumn 2000 floods was that the emergency planning arrangements worked generally well, with no deaths and relatively few injuries, despite the extent and severity of the flooding. There are, however, several ways in which arrangements could be improved and these will be considered as part of the ongoing national review.

It is widely acknowledged that recovery from major flooding incidents is the 'Cinderella' part of the whole process. Flood affected buildings may take many months to dry out and renovate, leaving people's lives disrupted for long periods. The social and economic effects are immense, not least on the health and well-being of those directly affected by floods. Insurance cover will help replace or restore the property of the individual householder or business but the wider issues of community recovery from flooding are hardly resourced at all.

Within the overall emergency planning framework, detailed flood emergency plans should be prepared for all significant settlements at risk from flooding. This task should be used as an opportunity to engage with, and raise awareness of, flood risk management issues among flood plain communities. Involving people in preparing emergency plans and developing initiatives, such as flood warden networks, are good ways of raising flood awareness among householders and businesses at risk. This should also include planning and resourcing for recovery from flooding, which needs to be given a higher priority.

As part of emergency plans, it is essential to have an effective, well-trained and well-equipped emergency work force for responding to emergency flood situations. The emergency work force can be productively used on routine maintenance and small contracts when not engaged on emergency duties. Further development of the cooperation that already exists between the Environment Agency, British Waterways and internal drainage boards would be valuable, especially when detailed knowledge of local conditions is vital in responding effectively to a flood emergency.

7   *Impact of climate change and catchment dynamics*

Frank Law

7.1   ASSESSMENT OF STUDIES

We do not wish to duplicate so many other climate change reviews (IPCC, 2001; UKCIP, 2000; UKCIP, 1998) but need to begin by pointing out that the repetition of a preferred scenario (e.g. wetter winters and drier summers) does not make it certain to occur. Although our climate is being disturbed by an inexorable rise in global mean temperature due to greenhouse gas emissions, caution is needed in future predictions if only because of the ability of volcanic eruptions of dust into the stratosphere to alter global temperatures. Such disturbances may not just cool the world temporarily but may have more subtle seasonal effects over different climate regions (Sadler and Grattan, 1999).

Historical work (Lamb, 1995) has revealed how our British climate has its apparent random variability constrained by some factors that are pseudo-cyclic, including shifts in North Sea wind strength that vary over two centuries and warm or cold centuries that have been noted since written records began.

Computer modelling work has proceeded on a staggering scale at several world-class meteorological centres, gradually coupling land and ocean systems to better reproduce known climates. The heat balance of the seas that dominates our weather takes perhaps 50 years to equilibrate to any external temperature change. No immediate threshold of change is thus likely to impose itself on British weather, governed as it is by the North Atlantic ocean circulation. The present known range of extremes — whether of tide, wave, surge, rain or snow — are daunting enough; an extra trend being added over time is a smaller complication for most British situations. The forthcoming

UKCIP02 climate change scenarios, featuring improved spatial (50 km) and temporal (daily) resolution, should considerably assist in this but further work is also required on developing probabilistic analysis of river flows. Arnell (1998) has well demonstrated how climate modelling can be taken through to realistic hydrological outcomes.

Political work, such as the Kyoto Agreement, has concentrated on reducing the emissions that disturb the global temperature regime. The authoritative Intergovernmental Panel on Climate Change (IPCC) reports (IPCC, 2001) have kept together the related findings of scientists along with the qualifications on the scenarios they paint for the next century.

DEFRA has issued guidance on the scope for future change in flood regimes that could be countenanced when scheme grant applications are made.

- *Sea level rise* — 6 mm/year in south-east England, falling to 4 mm/year in north-west England.
- *Flood peak magnitude* — an allowance of +20% increase in flood peak over 50 years (MAFF, 1999d).

There is an aptly named report entitled *To what degree can the October/November 2000 flood events be attributed to climate change?* (CEH and Meteorological Office, 2001), which gives a handy summary of the latest understanding of this topic in Britain, and states that

> The report characterises the October–November 2000 events as rare in terms of duration and extent. Effects of human-induced climate change are difficult to distinguish from natural variability; the results presented show some evidence of climatic influences on flooding, but give little indication of long-term trends. Climate modelling suggests that the frequency of large-scale rainfall extremes may have increased between 1860 and the present day, and that such increase will accelerate into the future. However, estimates of extremes based on long-term observations at individual sites have not, as yet, changed significantly. The report identifies some of the factors that remain to be assessed, particularly issues of the spatial patterns of flooding and seasonality.

This report details the top two, three and four month wet periods over the last 235 years. Slightly over half of these extreme events appear in the first half of the historic record, suggesting that higher temperatures since the industrial revolution have not yet changed the risk of seasonal widespread rainfall flooding in large basins.

However, the last 25 years have seen slightly more wet autumns, and far less cold dry seasonal conditions in the September–December period. Three long-term rain gauge sites on a transect down eastern Britain have all experienced a rising risk of any given rare one or seven day rainfall since, say, 1969 (CEH and Meteorological Office, 2001). However, it seems possible that this is due to increased variability under climate change rather than to a steady trend of the annual maximum event. While Odsey (Cambridgeshire) in the east shows no trend in its one day annual maximum rain, Penzance does. One reason that suggests itself is that rising North Atlantic sea temperatures may be affecting a westerly site like Penzance, but not those in the east of Britain. However, data from a further 11 UK sites do not show a clear spatial message in those terms.

Regrettably, few flood flow gauging stations cover sufficient years to be convincing about peak flow and runoff volume trends (Robson *et al.*, 1998). Those concerned about conditions along our best known river, the Thames, will be reassured that there is no sign of a trend in the one day annual maximum flow at Kingston upon Thames in either direction over the period since 1883 (when records of tolerable quality began).

Efforts have been made to run the Meteorological Office Regional Climate Model within a General Circulation Model of global climate, concentrating attention on the statistical distribution of rainfalls over the grid squares around York, Shrewsbury and Lewes. Areal rainfall 'observations' for these squares are used to calibrate the model under the present 1961–90 climate and then the model is run for the transiently higher carbon dioxide expected in the atmosphere over the 20 years at the end of the 21st century to see how rain intensities over realistic major basin areas could change. The resulting seven day total rain distribution shows a noteworthy increase in each case. Such research is still in its infancy; starting conditions and assumptions can have immense importance and, consequently, too great a weight should not yet be put on such results. The authors go no further than this summary (CEH and Meteorological Office, 2001)

The physically based model used in this study predicts that rainfall return periods for areal aggregations of 50 × 50 km will almost certainly reduce in a CO_2 enriched climate. For the period from 1860 to the year 2000, the changes may as yet be difficult to distinguish from natural variability. This does not present a contradiction with the results of other Chapters within this report.

7.2 THE IMPACT OF CLIMATE CHANGE ON FLOOD FLOWS AND WATER LEVELS

It is now quite clear that global mean temperature is rising (by 0·6°C since 1900 and a predicted further 1·5–2°C by the 2050s). This would suggest a more active and variable climate with higher rainfall depths. However, analysis of historic data has failed to show any clear trend, and modelled results based on Global Circulation Models (GCMs) show considerable variability about a possible overall pattern of drier summers and wetter winters. GCM data relate to large space increments (~300 km) and long time-steps (essentially monthly rainfall depths). It remains uncertain how impacts should be down-scaled to the catchment level, for example is any increase in rainfall due to more storms or more depth in each storm.

Various 'continuous simulation' studies have been performed using a range of GCMs and down-scaling methods, which suggested that 50-year flood peaks may be changed by between –30% and +20% in 2050. Most studies do show an increase in flooding in northern Britain, and those showing the largest reductions have usually been criticised in some respect.

Typical increases in peak flood water level on UK rivers would be in the range 0·2–0·8 m if the anticipated 20% growth in flood peak flow rates is eventually realised.

These figures vary considerably and factors include size of river, width of active flood plain and the amount of storage in the catchment. Generally, the wider the flood plain, the smaller the increase will be. Thus, the largest increases will occur on rivers which are contained by flood defences.

A programme of Catchment Flood Management Plans (CFMPs) is being implemented by the Environment Agency. The objective of each CFMP is to identify a preferred option for flood management in each catchment. The preferred options will consist of a combination of measures, which might include, for example, flood storage, local flood defences, flood warning, etc.

CFMPs include an assessment of the impacts of climate change and land use scenarios on flooding under existing conditions and with

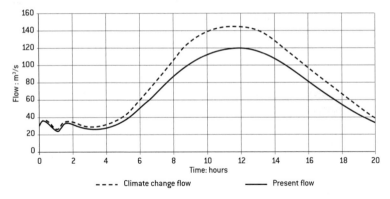

Figure 7.1. Estimated 100-year flood hydrographs on the Croal in Bolton, with and without climate change impacts — comparison of present and future flow conditions at TO10000

flood management options, to ensure that selected options are robust under both existing and future conditions. A Modelling and Decision Support Framework (MDSF) has been developed to facilitate the implementation of CFMPs. It includes catchment data management, guidance on catchment modelling, and calculation of the social and economic impacts of flooding.

The MDSF has been applied to the Croal catchment in north-west England, and Figure 7.1 shows the predicted impact of climate change on the estimated 100-year flood flow hydrograph in Bolton. The impact of the flow increase on flood levels was generally in excess of 0·3 m.

7.3   FUTURE NEEDS

The key climate change impacts on flood alleviation schemes include

- change in rainstorm intensity for a given frequency
- change in the prior wetness of a catchment at any particular storm season
- a different partition between rain and prior snow
- higher snowmelt rates

- lower expectation of frozen ground (or ice-jam flooding) and a shorter season for such surface impermeability
- higher mean sea level against which to discharge, with changes in tidal surge magnitude for a chosen frequency.

Other important themes that require more knowledge under climate change are

- rain duration
- multiple storm sequencing in a single season
- frequency and location of stationary heavy rainstorm systems.

We do not see in the working lifetime of most readers that sufficient change to energy use can prevent the measured slow rise of world temperatures. In particular, the growth of populations in the biggest nations will dictate much of the outcome. So we consider that it is not a question of deciding when climate change has become identifiable; rather, engineers and planners, with environmental science colleagues, must move to methods which allow for non-stationary statistics of key variables.

There is a real necessity to prove that global and local (under 10 000 km^2) rainfall fields can be modelled in both their mean and extreme frequency cases without 'fudge' factors being required in the calibration. Further research is required into the impact of seasonal catchment conditions on flooding, including the effects of climate change.

As financial damage and human distress is aggravated by the occurrence of multiple floods in a single season at any one community, methodologies must change away from annual maximum series (which neglect some flood data) to peaks-over-threshold series. This will be aided by the forthcoming development at the Centre for Ecology and Hydrology of tested continuous flood simulation methods.

7.4   CATCHMENT DYNAMICS

Why, if climate change has brought higher temperatures and potential evapotranspiration has the result not been drier soils and reduced floods? Only one part of the answer is because higher associated rain intensity acts in the opposing direction; Marsh (2001) shows that actual evaporation has not risen commensurately. Indeed, it may also be in any British catchment of substantial size, say 200 km^2 upwards, that there are always counterbalancing trends due to the range of anthropogenic activities, for example urbanisation provoking flood severity, but associated defence measures reducing them, or forest removal being countered elsewhere nearby by renewed tree planting, and so on.

7.5   TECHNICAL RESPONSE TO CHANGE

At its simplest, the 'wetter winters/drier summers' scenario over England and Wales logically implies that autumn floods will be reduced in frequency for any given size, with the reverse occurring in spring. That is an average expectation, not a prediction for the coming year. It is a consequence of outcomes for maximum soil moisture deficit and will be less noticeable where wilting-point conditions are reached in most summers anyway. It will be varied adversely if that additional soil dryness leads to soil crusting (as in the Foston Brook late summer flood in Derbyshire in the 1959).

Theoretical atmospheric considerations mean that a general rise in global temperature will lead to modest rises in the rain-producing mechanisms that give either small or large downpours but with little change to medium-size ones. This goes towards explaining why it is taking a considerable time to demonstrate that the measured world temperature rise has made itself manifest in more severe rainfall–intensity–frequency diagrams.

Winter floods, above and below ground, may be little affected in size for a fixed frequency but may be displaced until later in the season. This follows from the higher evaporation of the previous summer (in an average warmer world) and its consequences for soil-moisture-deficit size before a typical flood.

The Department for the Environment, Transport and the Regions (DETR, now DEFRA) monitored, over many years, the land use split between urban, forest and agricultural land. Changes have been remarkably slow on a national scale or in any major region. From a flooding aspect, further change (in England if not in Wales) could be more striking due to population growth and associated building than to countryside change or climate change. This is because urbanisation effects on flooding are one-sided, whereas with the other postulated changes there are normally 'swings and roundabouts' in the change of impermeability and storage. However, any alterations to the EU Common Agricultural Policy will need regular monitoring for their cumulative impact on flood generation, especially where intensification of production or set-aside creates drainage neglect.

The current 20% upsizing of the capacity of flood defence schemes to provide for climate change robustness is likely to be of the right order but community objectives of reducing risk and distress may require defence standards to be improved by at least that margin too.

Any technical review of flooding would be incomplete without recommendations addressing the effects of climate change. There is clear evidence that the floods considered extreme today will be less extreme in the future given the range in increase of future storm events coupled with change to land use.

An example is presented in Figure 7.2, which examines the flood risk at Pacific Quay on the River Clyde (Fleming and Guenin, 2001). A flood frequency analysis for the year 2000 is presented, then the effects of how this may change for conditions in the 2050s is examined by simply assuming a 10% increase in design event rainfall. The revised flood frequency analysis shows that 100–1 and 200–1 flood chances are halved to 50–1 and 100–1 flood chances, respectively, by the 2050s. This simple example clearly shows the importance of recognising the effects of possible future changes when designing.

The way forward is to accept that the change is occurring and using the available predictions to encourage design solutions that are less vulnerable to future change.

It is appropriate here to include the conclusions of the *Flood Estimation Handbook* team on trends in UK flood peaks (CEHW, 1999, Vol. 1, page 60, and Robson *et al.*, 1998).

- No significant trends were found in the annual count of peaks-over-threshold events for 1941–1980 and annual maxima for 1981–1990.
- The confounding effect of climatic variation means that trends associated with land-use change can neither be easily identified nor readily dismissed.
- Even though trend has not been detected, the observed year-to-year fluctuations in the data could have important consequences for flood design and trend analyses.

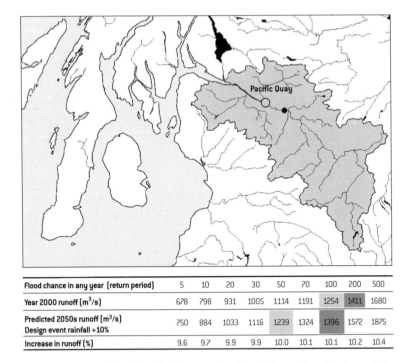

Flood chance in any year (return period)	5	10	20	30	50	70	100	200	500
Year 2000 runoff (m³/s)	678	798	931	1005	1114	1191	1254	1411	1680
Predicted 2050s runoff (m³/s) Design event rainfall +10%	750	884	1033	1116	1239	1324	1396	1572	1875
Increase in runoff (%)	9.6	9.7	9.9	9.9	10.0	10.1	10.1	10.2	10.4

Figure 7.2. A study of Pacific Quay on the Clyde shows that floods could be twice as likely in 50 years

- Although the study provided no conclusive proof that climatic change has affected fluvial flood behaviour in the UK, this does not mean that effects are not occurring.
- The sensitivity of assessments to climatic conditions in the period of record provides a strong reason for continuing data collection.

The authors of the above summary argue convincingly for a similar study of daily rainfall extremes, based on the necessary extension of computerisation of the nation's archive of daily rainfall records to those thousands of sites pre-1961.

The *Flood Estimation Handbook* is a landmark piece of work in that, for the first time, a nationally recognised methodology pools information from like catchments even though they are not adjacent.

This 'allows the user to judge whether a catchment may be intrinsically unusual, rather than unusual only in its largest observed floods' (CEHW, 1999, Vol. 1, page 61).

A recent study (Garrad, 2001) for the National Flood Warning Centre, Frimley, urged the use of POT3 as the trend indicator for floods, using a base period 1981–1995. POT3 is the flood magnitude that is exceeded on average three times per year over the given base period. The *Flood Estimation Handbook* provides summary statistics for this indicator (CEHW, 1999, Figs 21.5 and 21.6). It is obvious that short-term perturbations are the rule and that it may be some decades before all can agree that any trend has become established nationwide. It is far more likely that several specific catchments will first be seen to have become sensitive to climate change, just as urbanisation had radically affected some catchments during the new town expansion era after World War Two. Far more environmental indicators need to be established to serve the flood defence community, and it is believed that DEFRA intends to fund such research.

Marsh (2001) provides a good introduction to the use of long records for examining hydrological stability. In particular he shows two very long Chalk groundwater level records, for Therfield Rectory, Cambridgeshire, and Chilgrove, West Sussex, which, in the absence of local water supply abstraction, have been remarkably stable for many decades. This is despite their seasonal sensitivity to climate and changes of farming practice over their recharge areas. Whereas it might have been thought that rising temperatures would lead to higher evaporation and, hence, lower recharge, he shows that only potential evaporation has risen; corresponding actual evaporation from a typical mixed land surface has remained the same or lower, due to drier summers constraining the ability of vegetation to transpire over longer periods.

Good progress is now being made in simulating rainfall frequency relationships through embedding in GCMs a much closer Regional Climate Model grid, typically with a 50 km definition. It is likely that this is due to the far better representation of land topography, on which seasonal rain depths depend in Britain. However, the underlying difficulty of such complex simulations is the need to start any run with a valid initial condition set; if all climate physics is now transient then so much will remain uncertain.

It is to take a century scale view of flooding variability. Unfortunately, many time series are only available in homogenous

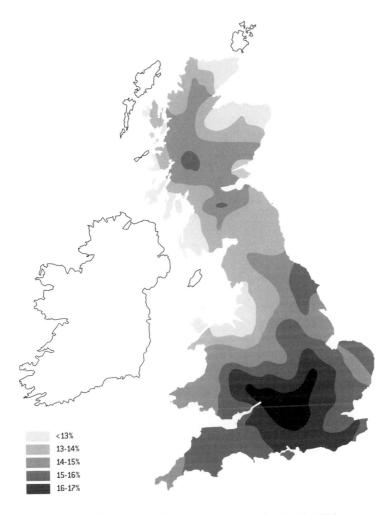

Figure 7.3. Coefficient of variation of annual rainfall 1881–1950

form for about 30 years, the very period that is most likely to suggest an upward trend has occurred if the very stimulus to analysis has been a recent major flood cluster. This effect is nicely illustrated by Osborn *et al.* (2000) where the recent 35-year rain statistics of the type underlying flood events are contrasted with those of a much longer period where the supposed trend well nigh disappears. Back in 1967, Law had already noted that successive standard 35-year rainfall average periods (1881–1915 and 1916–1950) could exhibit economically important variations; thus, the north-west England and south-west Scotland areas had mean annual rainfalls for those periods which differed by up to 14% (Binnie, 1967). Only by combining the two national maps of average annual rainfall into a 70-year version was an apparent stability found, or rather the contours of variability made geographic sense in relation to distance from the sea and mountain range shelter effects (Figure 7.3).

8 *Skills*

George Fleming

8.1 NEEDS

The types of skills required are far ranging and include

- well-informed and strategic thinkers at government level
- experts within universities, research institutes and consultancies
- Environment Agency staff with sufficient technical, operational and management skills (Environment Agency, 2000a)
- academic communities with the knowledge not only to teach and supply trained personnel in sufficient numbers to maintain the level of expertise within the UK but also, given the time and resources, to research new ideas.

All of the above are crucial to the delivery of a successful service. We add that a whole range of professions beyond engineering are involved in this requirement, although it seems that the growing shortage of students of civil engineering is a focus of the problem upon us.

The specific needs are in issues such as

- hydrology
- hydraulics
- fluvial processes
- mathematics
- modelling.

Skills often ignored include

- project and facility management
- risk assessment
- socio-economic analysis
- communication to the public.

Graduates are already in short supply now (e.g. 40% reduction in civil engineering admissions over the last five years) and this will get worse with the continuing national downward trend in applications to universities to study engineering and mathematics, a trend beginning some 20 years ago. The number of geographers and environmental scientists enrolling on the limited number of relevant MSc courses is however increasing slowly.

There is a skills shortage in river engineering, typically amounting to 20% of complement, which can only be addressed by increasing support to universities providing such courses. A taught MSc in flood risk management and river engineering, if accompanied by generous scholarships, could begin to turn around the situation within five years.

It is clear that the use of data and models will be essential tools for flood risk management. However, given the technical complexities of modelling and the depth of knowledge required at a local level concerning particular catchments, rivers and gauges, there are considerable challenges facing engineering staff — even with modern software.

It is recognised that the Environment Agency is not an emergency service, although in times of flood the public sometimes perceive it to be so. Given the greater skills required, the episodic nature of floods and the need for intensive forecasting and crisis management, use could be made of staff in hydrometric and modelling teams to develop and continually recalibrate models and to test them on a range of 'what if' scenarios. This would make most use of staff time, provide opportunities in career development and maintain core expertise at the place most needed, that is regional and local offices. It would also serve to redress the imbalance between the data and knowledge held by the framework consultants (operating over a relatively short term) and the Environment Agency staff (operating over the long term), as well as reducing the dependence on consultants and suppliers.

With the increased technical demands of management, an improvement in staffing levels within the industry should be considered, particularly with regard to senior technical and managerial posts concerned with flood management. A policy is required for attracting, training and keeping staff to higher technical and management levels, with a thorough understanding of the processes involved and skills in advanced modelling techniques (hydrological and hydrodynamic).

It is acknowledged that frequent movement of staff within the industry as part of the staff development programme has an adverse impact on the ability of the industry to respond to flood events. Local and detailed knowledge of rivers, flood defences, hydrology, and flood forecasting systems is important. The industry needs to consider how to foster technical skills without undermining promotional prospects.

8.2   TRAINING

Evidence was received that local government engineers and Environment Agency staff need training in *Flood Estimation Handbook* (CEHW, 1999) methodologies to greater depth (currently only around 20 fully trained and competent staff are available). Many, if not all, need extensive training in hydrodynamic models and all need additional training in running 'what if' flooding scenarios. It might also be desirable to undertake real-time simulation exercises, including the emergency response components. Training needs to be across all the partnering bodies of government, local authority, academic, water company and consultancy.

The charging for hydrological data has had an impact on training and the availability of the *Flood Estimation Handbook* CD for training students and young professionals has been restricted to single licence software to universities and training centres. This is based on a need to use Ordnance Survey maps in the software and the policy of recovery costs. It has the serious effect of placing *Flood Estimation Handbook* software beyond the reach of most university budgets where training in groups of up to 70 students is made very difficult.

Use should be made of in-house and external courses. There is value in supporting the academic community to establish strategic long-term skills in a number of fluvial and catchment modelling areas, along the lines of the National University of Ireland, Galway, and their international courses in river flow forecasting systems (O'Connor, 1995 and 1997).

However, the need for improved training extends well beyond the engineering profession. In particular, there is a need for improved understanding of flood risk assessment and flood risk management among a range of professions, such as town planners, architects, land surveyors, insurance and emergency managers. It is important that all the professions involved in flood risk management have a shared understanding of the issues and can work together to a common purpose.

9 *International*

George Fleming, Stephen Huntingdon, Donald Knight and
Frank Law

A comprehensive review of how other nations tackle flood risk
management is not possible here. Instead a sample of international
experience is offered in the hope that it will dispel some myths about
what can be achieved in societies needing to change and adapt.

The European Community research and development funds have
been a major feature of the 1990s (although few realise that the
principle of 'attribution' back to a sponsoring ministry leads to the
corresponding national research and development spend falling).
Flood topics have gained notable project funds, partly in response to
the wide range of Europe's states and accession countries that have
suffered outstanding disasters in recent times.

Project acronyms abound — here are a sample

- EFFS (http://effs.wldelft.nl/index.htm) — European Flood
  Forecasting System.
- EUROflood — see *Floods Across Europe* (EUROflood), 1994
  (eds E. Penning-Rowsell and M. Fordham) Flood Hazard Re-
  search Centre, Middlesex University.
- RIBAMOD (http://www.hrwallingford.co.uk/projects/RIBAMOD/)
  — Concerted Action on River basin modelling, management and
  flood mitigation.
- EUROTAS (http://www.hrwallingford.co.uk/projects/EUROTAS/)
  — Flood Risk Mitigation.
- RIPARIUS (http://www.nwl.ac.uk/ih/riparius/) — Risk of Inun-
  dation: Planning And Response Interactive User System.
- FLOODAWARE (http://wwwhh.lyon.cemagref.fr/public/pan-
  orama/95b.html).

- CADAM   (http://www.hrwallingford.co.uk/projects/CADAM/)
— Concerted Action on Dam Break Modelling.

The European Environment Agency has laid the groundwork for flood plain mapping in Europe by commissioning and publishing a continental scale digital rivers' map at a small scale with certain areas at a larger 200 000 pilot scale. Meanwhile, the contribution of the World Meteorological Organisation (WMO) has been to pass a resolution governing the free availability of any hydrological data on common rivers that is vital to life and property; in other words, upstream nations have a duty to warn downstream nations of any coming flood wave on which they have information. In an era where hydrometeorological agencies have been moving towards raising income by data sales, this was a key success for those who realise that public domain data can reduce damage loss and human distress.

9.1   FRANCE

France is characterised by having relatively few large drainage basins. Northern France, dominated by a chalk limestone geology, is subject to groundwater flooding in wet seasons. Southern France is notorious for severe thunderstorm floods over small tributaries. Its east-west transect covers from alpine to oceanic climates. As with many other European nations, it has paid more attention to its flooding history in recent years.

France had its first flood warning organisation as early as 1854, on the River Seine, with later expansion to the Loire and others. In the 1950s and 1960s, Electricite de France, the owner of many hydro dams, commissioned many physical hydraulic models of valleys to examine the potential for dam-failure flooding. France also has experience of operating flood warning systems for critical highway lengths, such as the Nice road tunnel which was known to be prone to flooding of the River Paillon.

Between the period 1982–1986, France almost doubled its cadre of specialist flood warning staff to 200. At that time it was estimated that the severe French annual flood damage bill could be reduced by 10% due to reactions of populations to warnings. The present-day expenditure of flood prevention efforts cost FFr1 billion per year, while flood damage costs FFr3 billion.

The national disaster mitigation programme is comprehensive and the taxation and property rating system includes a sum to contribute to handling disasters, including floods of all types. Under a law of 13 July 1982 (the year of a serious Seine flood) there is in effect a state-controlled flood insurance system. Victims of natural disasters are compensated by insurance companies out of an additional premium of 9% placed on the basic insurance premium on goods.

Vulnerability maps for communes were produced and, based on them, the French government took powers to prohibit construction work in high-risk areas. Flood plain limits are available for many places but not all. In 1987 the French Ministry of the Environment published a booklet *Operational Hydrology in France*, which included sections on flood protection and forecasting. Then their risk and vulnerability mapping programme for 1000 km^2 of urban land and 10 000 km^2 of rural land exposed to flooding was to be completed by 1994.

Although there has been effective development of integrated weather radar and satellite imagery on a European scale, it has largely been in the cause of meteorological forecasting.

9.2   NETHERLANDS

The vulnerability of the Netherlands to major flooding is far higher than in England and Wales. The continuing subsidence of the level of the reclaimed land and rise in sea level has resulted in about 25% of the Netherlands being below mean sea level. Without the protection of dykes and dunes along the coast, 65% of the country would be flooded daily. In addition, several major European rivers flow through the Netherlands, carrying floodwaters from other countries.

In order to protect against these potential floods and in recognition of the immense potential for flood damage if the defences are overtopped, the safety standards are considerably higher than found elsewhere. The coastal dykes in the central zone defend to a 10 000–1 chance flood per year (0·01% annual probability of flooding or 10 000-year return period), while the lowest defence level for some rivers is a 1250–1 chance flood per year (0·08% annual probability of flooding or 1250-year return period).

The sea defences are built to a much higher standard as coastal storm surges are more dangerous than river floods. Storm surges threaten the lowest, very densely populated and economically most important parts of the country. The sudden occurrence of storm surges leaves only a few hours to alert an emergency response procedure and evacuation of the population is impossible. Conversely, the warning time for river floods can be counted in days and allows for the necessary evacuation of the population.

Nevertheless, the prevention of fluvial flooding, although less severe than coastal, is a key issue to be solved. The problems of flood risk management are being looked at as part of the holistic management of whole rivers, considering also water quality and environmental issues. A strategy of 'making room for rivers' is being followed, with the acquisition of land either side of rivers so that new residential and commercial developments in the flood plain can be restricted. Furthermore, agricultural land within flood plains will also be reduced, allowing the development of natural habitats, landscape features and recreational facilities.

The strategy follows a sequential implementation of four main policies, with later policies being implemented if application of the former is unable to give the protection required

- redesign of planning of rural and urban areas
- provision of more room for water storage
- large-scale technical interventions
- controlled management of risk.

It is recognised that there is insufficient awareness of citizens and politicians to the risks being faced, exacerbated by pressures due to climate change. It is recognised by the professionals that the holistic approach being followed, with the strategic actions taken as above, will be more expensive in the short term than a piecemeal approach — but in the long term greater benefits will accrue. Similarly the fragmentation of the administrative bodies involved in flood risk management has been recognised and efforts are being made to reduce their number to simplify the lines of responsibility.

9.3   ITALY

Extending from the Alps in the north to the Mediterranean islands in the south and with varying land use types from alpine forest to agricultural plains, great emphasis is placed on agro-meteorology in Italy. This focuses on the relationship between growing crops and the prevailing climatic conditions in an effort to optimise agricultural capability through best practice.

At a national level, environmental legislation is set by the Italian Ministry of the Environment and the Agricultural Ministry. However, the Italian government has divided the country into 20 regions, 103 provinces and 8102 municipalities, each with varying degrees of power. Of these, five regions and two provinces are highly autonomous, with responsibility for their own flood protection, while 15 of the regional river basin authorities actually have the power to raise funding independently of central government. The foundations of flood forecasting in Italy are based upon integrated systems for real-time flood forecasting.

In 1925 the responsibility for meteorological observations and weather prediction was assigned to Italian Military Aviation but recent reforms have led to weather services being provided at a regional level, generally to provide support to agriculture. Regional river basins are governed by a river basin plan detailing the management of the catchment in terms of water and land use.

The Veneto river basin covers mountains in the north to low-lying plains around Venice. Meteorological stations throughout the catchment provide real-time rainfall data in conjunction with radar and satellite data. Agro-meteorological, hydrometric and water quality monitoring sites provide data to the central control organisation, which acts as a hydrometeorological forecasting service. Bulletins are issued twice-weekly for each of the 27 districts within the Veneto region, providing not only an assessment of the past three days' weather and a three-day forecast but also catchment maps of soil conditions in the area and other information vital for irrigation and crop planning. The regional authority also has responsibility for reservoir water levels and the opening and closing of sluices to control the river stage.

The Piedmont is a 25 000 km^2 alpine region and is home to over four million people. As a result of frequent, intense weather events leading to large-scale flooding and major damage to infrastructure, the regional authority set up an organisation in 1978 to deal specifically with flooding and the mitigation of damage from natural hazards. This organisation uses up-to-the-minute observations from a meteorological and hydrometric monitoring network, radar and sonde data as input to numerical meteorological forecast models.

A rainfall–runoff and river model (MIKE 11) exists for the Po Basin, covering an area of 37 000 km^2 within the Piedmont. This model is connected directly to the telemetry system and uses rainfall and temperature data from over 200 meteorological stations and water levels from 70 gauging stations, generated at ten-minute intervals. In addition to quantitative short-term precipitation forecasts, water levels and discharges for over 50 locations in the catchment are predicted for up to 48 hours ahead. Forecasts are updated hourly with no need for human intervention and a typical output is shown in Figure 9.1.

Both the Veneto and Piedmont river basins are using automated techniques to manage flood risk and issue flood warnings with sufficient lead times to allow the impacts of the flood to be mitigated as far as possible. A prime advantage of such an integrated hydrometeorological service is the focussed approach to catchment

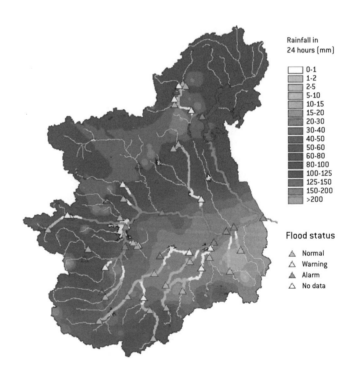

Figure 9.1. Flood forecast map for the Piedmont basin in Italy is generated automatically every hour

management and a more balanced treatment of the often conflicting needs of flood control, agriculture and water resources.

9.4   UNITED STATES

At federal level the United States has two main bodies to mitigate against flooding, the National Weather Service and the Federal Emergency Management Agency. The remits and responsibilities of these agencies are separate and well defined. The purpose of the National Weather Service is to provide meteorological, hydrological and climate services to the public, while the Federal Emergency Management Agency provides the federal focus for emergency management, from natural disasters to technological calamities and national security crises.

In terms of river basin forecasting, the core operational system of the National Weather Service is the Advanced Weather Interactive Process System — a highly automated system for processing and analysing a vast volume of data from station sensors, radar, satellite and other sources and using it to run large-scale river forecast models. All the information is disseminated and timely forecasts and warnings issued, both for severe weather and flooding.

The responsibility for operating the gauging station network lies with the US Geological Survey, a national scientific body with no regulatory responsibilities, while federal reservoir operation information is provided by the US Corps of Engineers. All these data are made available directly to the National Weather Service for input to forecasts.

The Federal Emergency Management Agency aims to reduce loss of life and property through a comprehensive, risk-based approach consisting of mitigation, preparedness, response and recovery (Lunan, 2001). The Agency only becomes directly involved on the ground during a flood after the event has been declared a disaster by the US President. For a disaster to be declared, a state governor must request federal intervention on the basis that the response and recovery capabilities of the state and local governments are overwhelmed. From this point onwards, the Agency is responsible for coordinating all flood response and recovery activities until the crisis is over.

The federal-level interests in flooding, water budget and water quality all filter down to state and local level and it is at this level that they are usually implemented. The Federal Emergency Management Agency aims to bypass state legislation and work directly with the communities at risk from flooding. In 1968 the National Flood Insurance Program was introduced in response to rising cost of taxpayer relief for flood victims and the increasing amount of damage caused by floods. The Program makes federally backed flood insurance available in communities that agree to adopt and enforce flood plain management ordinances to reduce future flood damage.

For the average year the Program is self-supporting with running costs and claims covered by the insurance premiums levied. No money from the insurance scheme is redirected to fund flood hazard reduction schemes — funding for these schemes comes from either federal or state government. In 2001, the Program operated over four million policies nationwide and estimate that a further two million people are at risk and uncovered. In 1999, there were 77 flood related deaths in the United States, 40 of which involved vehicles, and unadjusted losses were of the order of $5 million.

The scheme is based upon countrywide flood risk maps, constantly updated as communities join and instigate their own flood management schemes. Various zones are assigned to flood maps (Table 9.1), essentially covering

- base flood (100–1 chance flood or 1% annual probability of flooding or 100-year return period)
- moderate flood hazard areas (between 100–1 chance and 500–1 chance flood)
- minimal flood hazard (above 500–1 chance flood or 0·5% annual probability of flooding or 100-year return period).

Flood flows and levels are derived from historical recorded data wherever possible, alternatively if data are sparse then statistical methods are used to estimate the magnitude of defined flood events. Insurance premiums are set according to the zone and identified level of risk.

While flood forecasting and flood management in the United States are the responsibility of two distinct agencies, a high level of cooperation exists — particularly in the Emergency Managers Weather Information Network, which is run by the National Weather Service in partnership with the Federal Emergency Management Agency. This transmits a live stream of weather and other critical emergency planning information via radio, satellite and the internet

Table 9.1. Definition of United States flood map zones

Zone	Definition	Information available
A	Risk of inundation by the base flood event	No elevation or depths
A1–30	Risk of inundation by the base flood event determined by detailed methods	Base flood elevations
AH	Risk of inundation by the base flood shallow flooding where average depths are 1–3 ft (usually areas of ponding)	Base flood elevations
A0	Risk of inundation by the base flood shallow flooding where average depths are 1–3 ft (usually sheet flow on sloping terrain)	Average flood depths
A99	Risk of inundation by the base flood, but which will ultimately be protected upon completion of an under-construction Federal flood protection system	No elevations or depths
X	Moderate or minimal hazard from the principal flood source. However, could be flooded by severe, concentrated rainfall coupled with inadequate local drainage	
D	Unstudied areas where flood hazards are undetermined, but flooding is possible	

Note: For all zones, except D and X, flood insurance is mandatory

to the emergency managers in the field. The National Flood Insurance Program, by involving, educating and rewarding communities for good flood practice, increases public understanding and awareness of flood-related issues and advises people on how to minimise risk to themselves and their property.

9.5   JAPAN

The main characteristics of Japanese rivers compared with other countries is that they have steeper gradients and higher rainfall, with the result that flood runoff is large, rapid and significantly different from that in the river during normal periods of flow (Watanabe, 1998). Flood damage in Japan is therefore potentially very high and considerable efforts are taken to reduce its magnitude, particularly in urban conurbations, with major flood control projects dating back to 1896. Flood control measures are undertaken for each of the 109 first-class river systems, with the long-term objective of coping with a rainfall intensity likely to occur once in 100–200 years. For medium-sized and smaller rivers, the target is for rainfall intensities of 30–100 years. Flood projects are planned on a five-year planning cycle, with the ninth five-year plan (1997–2001) in progress. A River Council advises the Japanese Ministry of Construction prior to the formulation of each plan.

Japan has five Disaster Prevention Research Centres, set up in key centres, for the specific purpose of engaging in long-term research issues, many of which are related to rivers and flooding.

A particular problem of rapid economic growth has been the urbanisation of many flood plains, with the result that the damage potential has increased as more and more city and residential areas are sited behind flood defences. As a result 'integrated flood control measures' have been undertaken from 1975 to redress the problem. These have included

- engineered water retention basins
- improved pondage functions of the catchment area
- planning regulations covering land use
- constructing buildings that are safer with respect to flood damage
- provision of a warning and evacuation system.

Flood hazard maps have been produced since 1994, showing areal extent and depth of flooding.

In urban areas, rivers are often engineered into compound or two-stage channels as they pass through cities, as shown for the Toyohira river in Figure 9.2. Compound channels allow the main river to flow within a central channel for most of the year, maintaining depth and velocity of flow for environmental and geomorphological considerations, but in times of high flow the adjacent berms can be used to increase the conveyance capacity of the system. Two large embankments are needed at the outer edges of the berms to contain the water to the design flood depth (often up to 7 m on each flood plain). The berms have the added benefit of being able

Figure 9.2. Two-stage channel of the Toyohira river in Japan has wide berms for accommodating flood flows

to be used for most of the year for recreational and temporary purposes (e.g. golf links, playgrounds, sporting facilities and parking).

The embankments are necessarily large and on particularly vulnerable reaches of the Tone river, for example, 'super embankments' are used, some 12 m high and 200–300 m wide. The design flood discharge is $16\,000\,\text{m}^3/\text{s}$ and the floodway width between levees in the Tone river is some 700 m. Maintenance of the rationale for such investment is based on the fact that if the typhoon Catherine (1947) occurred again, and destroyed the same areas ($550\,\text{km}^2$), it would cause ¥15 trillion (£90 billion) worth of damage. The cost of maintaining the embankment is around ¥10 billion (£58 million) per annum.

In engineering terms, Japanese flood protection works are impressive. For example, the floodwater retention basins near the Uzuma, Omoi and Watarase rivers are very large, covering some 23 km^2, and have a combined storage capacity of 200 M.m^3. The Watarase reservoir alone covers 15 km^2.

The River Tone is the largest in Japan, with a catchment area of 16 840 km^2 and a length of 322 km (Kitagawa, 1998). The course and pattern of the river has been substantially altered since the construction of the first levees in 1457. Following the disaster of typhoon Catherine in 1947, the river is only capable of conveying floods of between a 30–1 chance to 40–1 chance of occurrence (2·5–3·3% annual probability of flooding or 30-year to 40-year return period), due to developments reducing the storage ability of the natural river. Although six dams have been constructed upstream, their storage capacity is insufficient. Construction of further dams and retention reservoirs is difficult due to environmental concerns. Consequently, preparation for the worst-case scenario is planned for, that is eventual failure of levees. Characteristic floods are being modelled carefully in order to provide information for suitable flood plain management and crisis management plans.

Extensive river training, including the cutting of new channels, shortening of meander bends and construction of entirely new drainage pathways to the coast have been undertaken in several rivers (e.g. Hiikawa, Yodo, Ishikari and Kushiro). It is instructive to note the high quality literature available to all visitors to Japanese river schemes and the public perception of the value of river engineering is probably greater in Japan than in any other country. The Kiso Sansen national government park has a specially constructed viewing tower to observe all the river works on the Ibi, Nagara and Kiso rivers. There is significant expenditure on educational equipment and information at such centres, raising the awareness of hydraulic engineering.

Urban drainage in many Japanese cities is unusual in that the adjoining rivers are often perched on ground higher than the city itself (e.g. Osaka). Thus, not only is flooding a particular threat but drainage also becomes a problem as well. The underground drainage system of central Tokyo has a three-stage flood control programme

- Stage 1: design for 50 mm/h (33% annual probability of flooding)
- Stage 2: design to 75 mm/h (6·7% annual probability of flooding)
- Stage 3: long-term objective of keeping Tokyo functioning with a rainfall intensity of 100 mm/h.

Since land is very costly, it is planned to use the underground conveyance capacity of wide arterial roads, connecting local surface rivers to the underground rivers. To drain water from the underground river, a pumping station with a capacity of 480 m^3/s will be located at the end of one route, near Tokyo bay. A temporary underground reservoir (tunnel), storing $540\ 000\ \text{m}^3$ will also be constructed. A management plan has been drawn up for control of the underground system, which is now operational.

9.6   SUMMARY

The practices of flood management in other countries highlight the variety of valid approaches and also the availability of fast, automated systems for the analysis and dissemination of forecasts and warnings.

One of the key differences between the approaches in different countries is the division of responsibilities for different aspects of the flood forecasting and management system.

The brief review of flood risk management in a few selected countries indicates support for an integrated approach. It also demonstrates that the use of river basin models is more widely accepted in the countries considered both for forecasting floods for design and real-time risk management.

10 Supply and delivery

Lindsay Frost

10.1 CURRENT ROLES AND RESPONSIBILITIES

This section is included as background for *our* view that flood risk management needs an established chain of responsibility, driven by a single responsible authority with the skill and experience to implement and deliver a sustainable flood risk management policy developed by the Government.

10.1.1 England and Wales

The roles and responsibilities of the various agencies involved in flood risk management in England and Wales are complex and, to many people, confusing. This perception was reinforced in the autumn 2000 floods, when a significant number of people did not know where to turn for advice and support when confronted with flooding problems.

At government level, DEFRA in England and the National Assembly for Wales determine policy for flood and coastal defence. This embraces

- setting policy aims, objectives and targets for the operating authorities
- providing strategic guidance
- grant aiding the funding of capital works which meet established criteria
- promoting a programme of research and development.

Policy on land use planning, including development in areas at risk from flooding, is set by the Department for Transport, Local Government and the Regions (DTLGR), which works closely with DEFRA to establish a coherent national policy in England on development and flood risk. In Wales, the National Assembly covers both functions.

Government policies on fluvial flood risk management are implemented through three types of operating authority, each with differing powers and duties

- Environment Agency
- internal drainage boards
- local authorities.

The powers available to the operating authorities are all permissive, meaning that they have the discretion to choose whether or not to carry out flood defence works. There is no statutory duty to carry out such works.

The *Environment Agency* has the role of implementing government policy and law and has a general supervisory duty on all matters related to flood defence in England and Wales. It also has permissive powers to carry out capital, maintenance and operational works to reduce the risks of flooding from designated 'main rivers' and the sea. The Environment Agency is also responsible for flood forecasting and the issuing of flood warnings to the public. In the planning field, the Environment Agency is a statutory consultee on the implications of development proposals on flood risk and the environment. The Environment Agency's statutory duty to survey matters relating to flooding, including mapping of areas vulnerable to flooding, assists its work in the planning field.

The Environment Agency exercises most of its flood defence responsibilities through a system of statutory *regional and local flood defence committees*. These committees determine priorities for, and spending on, flood defence works in their areas. The majority of representatives on the committees are from the constituent local authorities, which provide most of the funding through revenue-support-grant arrangements.

Internal drainage boards are statutory bodies that manage land drainage in areas of lowland England (e.g. the Fens of East Anglia, Somerset, Humberside) with special drainage needs. In all, there are over 230 boards covering 1·2 million hectares of the country. Within its defined area, each board undertakes flood defence works on watercourses other than 'main rivers'. Much of this work involves management of water levels through maintenance of a network of man-made channels and pumping stations.

Local authorities have powers to maintain or improve flood defences on watercourses, which are not 'main rivers' or within internal drainage districts. In addition, they have certain powers of enforcement over private landowners adjacent to watercourses to ensure efficient drainage. The degree to which these powers are used varies significantly up and down the country. DEFRA's *High Level Targets for Flood and Coastal Defence* (MAFF, 1999b) seeks to codify each authority's approach through a publicly available statement.

The local authorities also have other important roles and responsibilities in managing flood risk. As local planning authorities, they prepare development plans and determine planning applications. In exercising this role, they have to consider the implications of proposed development on flood risk in accordance with national planning policy in *Planning Policy Guidance Note 25, Development and Flood Risk* (DTLR, 2001). The local authorities also administer the Building Regulations, which set standards for drainage from buildings. As highway authorities, they are responsible for draining highways. This includes managing water flows onto, and from, highways, and responsibilities for certain bridges and culverts. The local authorities also coordinate emergency planning in their areas, including response to, and recovery from, major flood emergencies (Table 10.1).

The *emergency services* (police, fire, ambulance and coastguard) have a key role in emergency planning and response to major flood emergencies, through participation in joint agency command and control teams and relief-rescue action in the field.

Notwithstanding the complex structure of statutory bodies outlined above (see also Table 10.1), it is important to remember that the primary responsibility for safeguarding land and other property against flooding remains with the *private landowner*. Individual property owners are also responsible for managing their land so as to prevent adverse drainage impacts on nearby land. Any private flood defences remain the responsibility of the riparian owner, unless adopted by the operating authorities.

The *water utility companies* are responsible for foul drainage through adopted sewers and for surface water drainage from

Table 10.1. An outline of emergency coordination arrangements in response to a major flood incident

Level	Role and responsibilities
GOLD — Strategic Coordinating Group	Provides forum for sharing of information and corporate decision-making
	Chaired by Police Commander and involves senior officers from county council, emergency services and other agencies
	Coordinates actions over wide area (e.g. county)
SILVER — Incident Command Post	Local command base, close to scene of incident
	Chaired by senior police officer and includes senior officers from emergency services, local authorities and utility companies (Chair may revert to local authority later)
	Coordinates action over local area
BRONZE — Operational Command	Appointed officers from appropriate agencies who control and coordinate action at the scene (e.g. cordons and evacuation or pollution control)
	Reports back to Silver

development. In flood conditions, the sewer systems can become overloaded with a mixture of floodwater and sewage leading to backing up, overflow and flooding. The utility companies work with the other operating authorities to resolve these problems.

Considerable cooperation and coordination exists between each of the agencies involved in flood risk management. A review *should* be undertaken to determine what improvements could be introduced to secure even better partnership between the agencies involved in flood risk management and to provide clear communication to the public of the network of responsibility and advice in time of flood.

10.1.2 Scotland

The roles and responsibilities in relation to flood risk management are significantly different in Scotland to those in England and Wales. At government level the Scottish Executive is responsible for developing national policy in relation to flood risk and providing resources for such policy to be implemented. This role is specifically carried out by the Scottish Executive Environment and Rural Affairs Department (SEERAD).

In Scotland the lead role in fluvial and coastal flood risk management is taken by the relevant local authority or island council. The Flood Prevention (Scotland) Act 1961 empowered the regional and island councils to take any measures they considered reasonable to prevent or mitigate against flooding of *non-agricultural* land. This was updated and amended by the Flood Prevention and Land Drainage (Scotland) Act 1997, which imposed a duty on the local authorities to assess watercourses and to maintain these in such a way as to reduce the likelihood of flooding. Existing flood defences may be maintained and repaired but any improvements or new flood defence works require the development of a *Flood Prevention Scheme*. The details of such schemes must be made available to the public, and approved by the Secretary of State for Scotland. Any objections or appeals are dealt with at Public Inquiry.

For agricultural land and forestry, the responsibility for flood protection lies with the riparian landowner and permitted development rights exist for land drainage and flood protection; grants for such work are administered by SEEFAD. However, any flood protection measures can have effects downstream and the farmer must obtain written permission from the Scottish Environment Protection Agency (SEPA) and other statutory consultants, such as Scottish Natural Heritage (SNH), if the site has any special conservation designations.

SEPA was formed under the Environment Act 1995, replacing the existing River Purification Boards. Whereas the Environment Agency in England and Wales have a statutory duty to implement government policy on flood-related issues, assessment of flood risk in Scotland is classed as one of SEPA's functions *only as far as SEPA considers it appropriate*. SEPA do, however, have a duty to provide guidance and advice on flooding to local authorities on request.

Local authorities have the powers to form local Flood Appraisal Groups, drawing on local expertise from a range of sources, including

SEPA, landowners and insurance companies. These flood appraisal groups are concerned with measures to reduce damage caused by flooding and provide informal guidance and practical advice to local authorities on flood-related issues. Local authorities also have the responsibility for the maintenance and upkeep of all watercourses with the exception of sewers and water mains, which are under the remit of the Water Authorities.

Under the Town and Country Planning (Scotland) Act 1972, planning authorities have the power to consider flooding issues when considering planning applications and appeals. The *National Planning Policy Guideline on The Planning System* (NPPG1) further enforces the need for planning authorities to consider the safety of the community, which involves flood risk. NPPG7, *Planning and Flooding*, further developed the existing guidance to encourage the planning authorities to use their powers to guide, regulate and control development in areas at risk from flooding. It promotes a precautionary approach to decision making and, as in England and Wales, emphasises that the primary responsibility for protection against flooding lies with the property owner.

SEPA operate the river gauging network and flood warning systems in Scotland, and issue flood warnings to the local authorities and the police as appropriate. The local authority takes the lead role in the management of the flood event, coordinating responses and mitigation measures in conjunction with the emergency services (police, fire, ambulance and coastguard). SEPA have recently opened a *Floodline* to provide the public with flood warning information, similar to the service provide by the Environment Agency.

With the impending implementation of the Water Framework Directive, SEPA is likely to be responsible for the development of river basin management plans, which will address the management of the catchment as a whole. Flood risk management will be a major aspect of such plans. A review of the roles of the local authorities and SEPA in flood risk management would clarify the roles of each organisation in planning for and managing flood risk.

10.2   INSURANCE

10.2.1 *Introduction*

Insurance risk has three elements

- risk to human life
- risk to buildings (and their contents) and other physical infrastructure
- financial risk.

In the vast majority of cases, the costs of physical damage and financial losses from river flooding have been readily insurable in the commercial market. As such, the widespread expectation of, and reliance upon, continued availability of insurance cover has been an important element in the overall approach to flood risk management in England and Wales.

Although there is no statutory requirement to do so, the UK insurance industry generally aims to cover as many potential customers as possible (unlike many other countries in the EU and elsewhere, there is no public insurance provision). Nevertheless, only 70–80% of the UK population has insurance against flooding. Only a very small proportion of the 'non-insured' has been refused cover by the industry. The vast majority are people who choose not to buy, or cannot afford, appropriate insurance cover.

The level of exposure to river and coastal flood risk in England and Wales is significant (see Table 10.2).

In a typical year, insurance claims for river flooding in the UK total around £150 million. However, events such as the Easter 1998 and autumn 2000 floods can push this much higher, with the latter leading to claims in excess of £700 million (Milne, 2001). These serious flood events have had a significant effect on the insurance industry's recent profitability. Nevertheless, these flood claims still fall well below those incurred during large-scale storm events, such as those of 1987 and 1990, where damage was even more widespread and costly.

10.2.2 *The industry viewpoint*

The Association of British Insurers has long been concerned about the threat of inland flooding and that climate change and pressure for development in vulnerable locations may increase the industry's future exposure to risk. As a result, the Association has commissioned research into flooding issues and works with government agencies to improve understanding. The aim of this research is to

Table 10.2. Exposure to river and coastal flooding in England and Wales (source DEFRA, 2001)

Land area of England and Wales (km^2)	12 500
Percentage of total area exposed to flood risk	9·5%
Number of homes	1 773 000
Number of commercial properties	136 000
Agricultural land (million hectares)	1·3
Property value (£ billion)	*208*
Agricultural value (£ billion)	*7*
Total value (£ billion)	*215*

- identify levels of risk and exposure
- influence government flood defence and planning policies
- help insurers continue to provide cover to customers.

In future, the market price of insurance will increasingly be correlated to the individual risk of the customer's property.

Many of the aims of the insurance industry are in sympathy with the aims of the agencies responsible with flood risk management. However, many of the properties and much of the land at risk to flooding arise from historical land use practice. The issue of flood risk management in the future will still require existing properties to have some indemnity against flooding. That insurability will remain an important tool in balancing the ability to mitigate the risk by defences and good management with the extreme floods that are likely to occur.

10.2.3 The consumer viewpoint

The general effect of the high insurance claims arising from flood damage in the last two or three years will be a small increase in premiums. This should cause few problems for the great majority of insurance customers, who live in locations that are not vulnerable to flooding.

The effects of the insurance industry's increasing concerns about flood risk will fall overwhelmingly on those householders and businesses living or working in higher-risk flood plain locations, or considering buying or occupying property there. The effects will be either more expensive, reduced or withdrawn insurance cover, particularly if 'redlining' is introduced on a wide scale.

People in the vulnerable areas are understandably worried by the prospect of insurance cover being progressively withdrawn. This is adding to the stress and anxiety suffered by those affected by the autumn 2000 floods. Where property is being bought and sold, the insurance companies do not feel the same obligation to provide cover as with established customers. There is some evidence that this is blighting sales in what is already a difficult market for vendors. On the positive side, it will act as a disincentive to developers when considering the potential of flood prone areas.

There are fears that 'redlining' may become a self-fulfilling threat in that, in many cases, it is unrealistic to expect the authorities to implement major new flood alleviation schemes within the two-year time-scale set by the Association of British Insurers, particularly if a wider catchment perspective is necessary to identify the right scheme.

Feedback from householders and businesses affected by recent flooding has drawn a generally positive picture of the insurance companies' performance. Most companies have performed well but others have been criticised by their clients (Warwickshire County Council, 1998; Magness, 2001). Some common complaints have been

- slow response following flood emergencies
- loss adjusters under-resourced to meet clients' needs
- slowness in making interim payments
- insufficient quality control over appointed builders
- no account of customer efforts to reduce risk by making their property more flood resistant.

10.3 KEY ISSUES IN SUPPLY AND DELIVERY OF FLOOD RISK MANAGEMENT

The following key issues arise from our consideration of the current position on supply and delivery of flood risk management in England and Wales.

10.3.1 Do we need to review roles and responsibilities for flood risk management?

With over 700 authorities having some responsibility for flood alleviation (aside from all those authorities with a potential involvement with emergency response), there is a clear fragmentation of responsibility in flood risk management in England Wales.

Whereas the strategic policy is delivered by DEFRA's *High Level Targets for Flood and Coastal Defence* (MAFF, 1999b), there is no single authority charged with the strategic delivery of the service. The consequences of the fragmentation appear in the confusion of the public concerning responsibility and the thin spreading of the skill resource across the large number of authorities carrying responsibility.

It is generally agreed within the flood management community that awareness of flooding by the public at risk is essential if we are to mobilise their cooperation in participating in flood preparedness and emergency response. To achieve the required results, this awareness must be sympathetic to the professionals asking for public cooperation. The fragmentation of responsibilities causes confusion and even positive alienation when authorities start arguing about responsibility and deny a timely resolution of flooding problems. To mobilise the goodwill and support of the public, it is essential that a clear and consistent delivery of service is obviously apparent. The cause of flooding is irrelevant to those exposed to it.

The number of responsible authorities across which the resource has to be spread exacerbates the skill shortage highlighted earlier. Indeed, some authorities with inherited responsibilities for flood alleviation do not have any competent expertise within that authority due to staff development policies and outsourcing decisions.

Attention is drawn to the excessive fragmentation because it impacts directly on the technical aspects. We need to improve the awareness of the public at risk from flooding to encourage them to play their part in the holistic response to flood protection we have identified and supported as essential. The public needs to be motivated to take precautions and be prepared to minimise the effects of flooding. This is likely to be less than enthusiastic if a lack of clarity over the role and responsibility of the professionals is at all apparent. Similarly, the technical response to flooding in this century will be totally dependent on the quality and number of appropriately qualified staff — and on the efficient and effective deployment of those staff.

It is not within our role and expertise to specify how such a strategic delivery of flood risk mitigation should be structured. But we are convinced that a single authority must be responsible for the strategic execution of those duties necessary to meet the strategic policies and targets set, and those responsible must be accountable.

The single authority need not be a new body but could be an extension of the role of an existing participant. It is also not necessary for the new authority to take all existing powers of existing bodies — but it should have overarching responsibility for consistent action with a common system of prioritisation. Similarly we are convinced that, although the delivery of this strategic response has to have a strong unified voice, it must also have effective regional and local participation and influence to ensure maximum local involvement.

10.3.2 *How can we improve public awareness of roles and responsibilities?*

As already noted, there is some public confusion as to the roles and responsibilities of the various operating authorities involved in flood risk management. This is not surprising given the 'number of bodies involved and the fact that they have separate budgets rather than a single flood protection programme' (National Audit Office, 2001). The confusion is compounded by the historical, and now seemingly arbitrary, way in which watercourses are classified as either 'main rivers' or 'ordinary watercourses', with different agencies having responsibility for them and often working to different standards with different budgets.

Given the complexity of existing arrangements, it is perhaps unreasonable and unrealistic to expect ordinary members of the public to get to grips with such a fragmented system, particularly in the stressful circumstances of a flood incident. Instead, in an era of 'joined-up government', it is incumbent on the various agencies to work together to offer the public what Ministers have called a 'seamless and integrated' service. This can be achieved in two ways

- institutional reform to clarify and simplify roles and responsi-bilities
- improved partnership arrangements to offer a 'one-stop shop' service to the public.

The first alternative is discussed in the previous section. The second also has merit and we recommend that the various authorities continue to work together to develop single points of contact and information on flood-related matters to make it easier for the public to get the help they need.

10.3.3 Are sufficient resources available to deliver a national strategy for flood risk management?

The Government's own studies indicate that there is a need for increased investment in flood and coastal defences if present standards of protection are to be maintained. Climate change may make this need even more acute (DEFRA, 2001). Current plans are that DEFRA funding on these items will increase from £76 million in 2000/1 to £114 million in 2003/4.

All this is welcome, but increased spending will have to be sustained for many years ahead and not cut back if we are fortunate enough to have some relatively flood-sparse years. The new catchment flood management plans will also drive a need for sustained, integrated expenditure over a long period. We must leave behind the old cycle of under-investment in new flood alleviation works and failure properly to maintain existing ones, until broken by a serious flood event.

However, we need to go beyond maintaining and improving the country's physical infrastructure to manage flood risk. The country also needs to look at increasing the resources it puts into training, developing and retaining the staff it needs to operate flood management successfully.

11   The future for flood risk management

11.1   PRESENT CONDITIONS

Current methods of estimating and reducing flood risk show that there is a serious inadequacy in representing the dynamic effects of land use changes, catchment processes and climatic variability. There is also a reluctance to use available computer models to provide greater insight into the sensitivity of flood risk for a combination of conditions.

A more strategic catchment-based approach is essential in tackling fluvial flood alleviation.

There is a very significant impact of flood defences in both the natural and built environment. The impact has been to reduce the risk of flooding and, in most cases, flood defences have been sympathetic to the built environment and, indeed, have become an integral part of a sustainable built environment. In the natural environment, the impact of flood defences may, in general terms, have been less successful in alleviating rural flood risk. There is a clear need to provide capacity for rivers to respond to flooding in both the rural and built environment by the more careful balance of land use through redevelopment.

Sustainable flood risk management can only be achieved by working with the natural response of the river basin and providing the necessary storage, flow reduction and discharge capacity. Floods can only be managed, not prevented, and the community must learn to live with rivers.

There is evidence of the significant impact that climate change is having on the rainfall, evaporation, storage and runoff within catchments. It is essential that best practice in flood estimation has the effects of climate change designed into it.

There is a need for a more integrated approach to flood risk management, and a need for greater confidence in river basin modelling both for flood assessment and real-time flood management in the UK.

Fluvial flood risk management needs to be a holistic process that considers flooding from the point rainfall hits the ground to the place it is finally discharged into the sea. It needs to recognise, evaluate and take into account the human dimension as well as the technical and economic cases for interventions, and the environmental impact of these. It requires a full understanding of all the physical processes involved and the ways in which these are changed by human activities, from agriculture to urban development. It needs a trained and motivated body of professionals at all levels, equipped with the necessary tools and resources. Finally, it needs the understanding and cooperation of the people who will benefit.

The main issues for flood risk management within the UK are outlined in the following sections and are drawn from *Learning to Live with Rivers* (ICE, 2001).

11.2 RAISING FLOOD AWARENESS

11.2.1 The recent periods of widespread and sustained flooding have raised awareness of the damage and distress that can occur. It is crucial that we take advantage of this raised state of awareness to communicate the realities of flood risk and how we manage this risk. This communication process must be maintained indefinitely to ensure that time does not diminish the level of awareness that is of considerable help in reducing the impacts of flooding.

11.2.2 The Environment Agency's initiatives in raising awareness of fluvial flooding should be supported, and a long-term education initiative is required to stress that flood risks cannot be removed and to explain the uncertainties inherent in flood forecasting. With a sufficient level of knowledge, flood-prone members of the public could themselves become involved in the processes of emergency planning and flood risk management, bringing real engagement of those at risk.

11.2.3 In terms of communicating the likelihood of flooding, the use of 'return period' is unhelpful to lay persons. However, understanding of odds and probabilities is widespread, arising in many games and sports involving chance and gambling. Odds of 3–1 for a horse to win a steeplechase are equivalent to a 3 out of 4 chance or 75% probability that the horse will not win and a 1 in 4 or 25% probability of the horse coming in first. Therefore, it is recommended that, instead of referring to the 100-year flood, flood events are referred to in terms of probabilities, thus the 100–1 chance flood or 1% probability of flooding in a given year, regardless of any recent severe occurrences.

11.2.4 Historical flood level marking is an effective means of raising flood awareness in communities.

11.2.5 Flood risk maps are a valuable source of information for the public and for those involved in development control and flood risk management. The present maps are not accurate or detailed enough to give confidence in the guidance that they provide. The Environment Agency should give high priority to this initiative to ensure that the maps give accurate, up-to-date and reliable information.

11.2.6 The Environment Agency, recognising the legal implications, should move ahead to refine flood plain mapping to indicate to the public which areas have some measure of flood defence with the associated quantifiable risk.

11.2.7 There is a complex division of responsibilities in flood risk management and the authors recommend the provision of a 'one-stop shop' for public access and information.

11.3 PROMOTING THE HUMAN DIMENSION

11.3.1 The human distress and health damage caused by flooding has been overlooked in the strictly economic approach adopted to assess the benefits of flood mitigation interventions. This human cost should be built-in to future benefit-cost assessments, so that the true worth of interventions is established. Preliminary research shows that the intangible costs of flooding are of the same order as the tangible costs.

11.4 PLANNING FOR FLOODS

11.4.1 The authors endorse the risk-based, sequential approach to development on flood plains advocated in *Planning Policy Guidance Note 25, Development and Flood Risk* (DTLR, 2001). In particular, we support the need for flood risk assessments to accompany proposals for new development in flood plain locations linked, as appropriate, with models and data deriving from the process of preparing catchment flood management plans.

11.4.2 A more strategic-based catchment approach should be promoted, of which the initiative for catchment flood management plans is an important element. However, the time needed to develop catchment plans and the follow-up initiatives should not be used as a reason to delay the implementation of flood defences and other interventions that are already in the pipeline.

11.4.3 While much effort is rightly going into establishing a sound methodology for preparing catchment flood management plans, producing the plans is not an end in itself. More consideration needs to be given to the practical issues of ensuring that there are the leadership and professional skills, stakeholder commitment, partnership structures and financial resources to turn the plans into action on the ground.

11.4.4 Flood storage areas should be identified as a recognised land use for inclusion in local plans. Agri-environmental schemes should be promoted where appropriate as elements in flood risk management, an attractive complement to farming in financial terms and a means of promoting biodiversity.

11.4.5 Within the overall emergency planning framework, detailed flood emergency plans should be prepared for all significant settlements at risk from flooding. This task should be used as an opportunity to engage with, and raise awareness of, flood risk management issues among flood plain communities. Involving people in preparing emergency plans and developing initiatives such as flood warden networks are good ways of raising flood awareness among householders and businesses at risk. This should also include planning and resourcing for recovery from flooding, which needs to be given a higher priority.

11.4.6   It is essential for the Environment Agency to have an effective, well-trained and well-equipped emergency work force for responding to emergency flood situations.

11.4.7   The authors support *Planning Policy Guidance Note 25, Development and Flood Risk* (DTLR, 2001) for encouraging planning authorities to require a 'drainage impact assessment' for all new developments. This would cover all drainage related issues in sufficient depth to ensure that appropriate and sustainable solutions are incorporated into the development proposals.

11.4.8   The performance indicators established to monitor the implementation of DEFRA's *High Level Targets for Flood and Coastal Defence* (MAFF, 1999b) should be expanded to include the number of households flooded each year. The present approach is too focused on economic benefit and needs to recognise the human distress and health effects of flooding.

11.5   DESIGNING FOR FLOODS

11.5.1   A wider application of risk-based methods is encouraged by both clients and professionals involved in flood risk management. This will involve increased competency levels and adherence to best practice.

11.5.2   For the future, it is no longer acceptable to design flood defence schemes on the basis of a single event (the design event). For the future, scheme design should extend the analysis to look at sensitivity to flows higher than the present design flow to take into account climatic and land use changes and to ensure that the impact of extreme floods is fully addressed as part of the design process.

11.5.3   Design engineers should be encouraged to take advantage of the power of the *Flood Estimation Handbook* (CEHW, 1999) techniques to explore the sensitivity of the flood regime to climate change and land use.

11.5.4   The link between stage (hydraulics) and discharge (hydrology) is of particular importance. Powerful methods such as the *Flood Estimation Handbook* (CEHW, 1999) lack a complementary approach in hydraulics and this imbalance must be rectified if progress is to be made in designing and modelling for flooding events.

11.5.5   All conveyance and storage options should be considered in every case where solutions are being sought for a fluvial flooding problem. This should include land use change such as the option of abandoning houses and other buildings that have been constructed in the flood plain.

11.5.6   In circumstances where it is appropriate to provide engineered defences to protect significant numbers (i.e. hundreds) of people in a contiguous community, the aim should be to provide a high standard of defence, even if the economic analysis reveals that a lower standard would yield a larger benefit-cost ratio. It is recommended that the target should be based on providing protection against the 100–1 chance flood in any year as a minimum.

11.5.7   The authors recommend that an assessment of the role of sustainable urban drainage systems and the impact of more frequent and longer duration river floods on sewers and sewage pumping stations is undertaken. Development of national standards for the infrastructure of sustainable urban drainage systems will allow easier adoption by the utility companies and local authorities.

11.6   ASSET MANAGEMENT

11.6.1   There is evidence of under-investment in maintenance of flood defences over recent years and of a lack of planning and programming of maintenance in accordance with need. This trend needs to be reversed so that existing flood alleviation schemes perform as designed. All interventions should be planned with a full appreciation of operation and maintenance requirements and resulting whole-life costs. This process will be facilitated by the use of risk-based analytical techniques and regular condition surveys.

11.6.2   The authors strongly support the establishment of a national database of flood defence assets. This will be invaluable for future operation and maintenance activities and for planning the eventual replacement of existing flood defence infrastructure. To ensure that this initiative does not founder, consideration should be given to placing the responsibility for gathering information on all defences with a single agency, regardless of ownership.

11.6.3 In view of the high risk of flooding caused by blockages of culverts and trash screens, it is recommended that all critical culverts be assessed for this risk. In assessing the options for overcoming the flood risk posed by blockages, we should not shy away from reclaiming urban channels that have been culverted or encroached upon by development.

11.6.4 The management of earthen flood defences should be the subject of research and development so that future maintenance, repair and replacement programmes can proceed on the basis of sound knowledge. This research should proceed in parallel with research into the failure modes of earth embankments so that increased understanding can be used to inform flood risk management when embankments are subjected to high water levels.

11.7 RESEARCH

11.7.1 The authors commend the DEFRA/Environment Agency research and development programme and recommends the level of funding in research and development should be built up to the figure established in the Penning-Rowsell Report and maintained at that level, at least until the next review (namely, £5·2 million each year).

11.7.2 The present structure of the research councils (Natural Environment Research Council, Engineering and Physical Sciences Research Council, Social Research Council, Medical Research Council, Biological and Biomedical Sciences, and Office of Science and Technology) has failed to nurture cross-boundary projects in the area of flood risk management, especially with respect to technical, health, social and environmental impacts. It is recommended that the structure of the research councils should be reviewed.

11.7.3 Consideration should be given to a long-term strategy for developing research skills within the UK for flood analysis. Considerable gaps have been identified in our knowledge and a move to a solution-orientated culture by all concerned with flood risk management will enable these gaps to be filled. Greater collaboration on research and development between the Environment Agency, DEFRA, academia and research institutes needs to be promoted. In particular, greater collaboration between the Natural Environment Research Council and the Engineering and Physical Sciences Research Council, which would join a 'pure science' approach with an 'engineering science' approach, is urgently needed for fluvial problems.

11.7.4 Recent competitive research contract practice in the Natural Environment Research Council and the Engineering and Physical Sciences Research Council has been to announce a multi-million pound theme and then let the spending be on a myriad of relatively disconnected topics loosely within that theme. Applied flood research, of key value to the community, needs a more managed approach. The success of the *Flood Studies Report* (NERC, 1975) is often over-looked. The next major target should be 'long-sequence flow simulation', covering river-level–velocity–energy relationships, with full visualisation (as with building design).

11.7.5 More research is needed into the interaction of sewer and piped drainage systems and the rivers into which they discharge in flood events. This is an area of research that inevitably falls between two schools. Contact should be established between the DEFRA/ Environment Agency research and development programme and the UK Water Industry Research to explore the possibilities for a jointly funded research programme.

11.7.6 Further research is required into the impact of seasonal catchment conditions on flooding, including the effects of climate change.

11.7.7 A particular area for further study is the link between land use and flooding, so as to have confidence in policy changes that could lead to a significant reduction of flood risk. Whole-catchment modelling should be undertaken with greater vigour to address this issue.

11.7.8 It is recommended that research be progressed to enable monetary values to be attributed to the cost of the health and social distress caused by flooding, or the benefit of its avoidance.

Recent, ongoing and proposed DEFRA/Environment Agency research projects (2002)

Fluvial, estuarine and coastal processes theme
- Estuary morphology — survey and modelling for managed set-back site
- Additional monitoring at the Tollesbury site
- Development of predictive tools and design guidance for mixed beaches — Stage 2
- Estuaries Research Programme — Processes Component Phase 2
- Sediments and Habitats Concerted Action
- Flood Hydrology Concerted Action
- Coastal Concerted Action
- Frieston Managed Realignment
- Sand transport and morphology of offshore sand mining or borrow pits/areas (SANDPIT)
- Revitalisation of the *Flood Studies Report/Flood Estimation Handbook* Rainfall–Runoff Method
- Guidebook of Applied Fluvial Geomorphology
- Impact of Recent Floods on River Morphology and Habitats
- Evaluation of breach processes at Porlock shingle ridge

Policy development theme
- Updating and modernising the 'Yellow/Blue/Red Manuals' for appraising coastal defence and flood alleviation works
- Prediction of Future Coastal Evolution for SMP Review
- Proposed Scheme Prioritisation System Review Project
- The appraisal of human related intangible impacts of flooding
- Improving public awareness and understanding about flood risk
- Implementing Managed Realignment as a Strategic Flood and Coastal Defence option
- Consistent Standards of Flood Defence for Flood Cells
- Flood Plain Management Manual Phase 1

- Testing the criteria for the designation of heavily modified waters for the Water Framework Directive Agency input to EU project
- Wise use of wetlands
- National Environmental Assessment Handbook Update
- Assessing the costs and benefits of flood defence

Broad-scale modelling theme

- Estuary Research Programme — Tidal River Bathymetry (Humber)
- Generation of Spatially Consistent Rainfall Data — Refinement and Testing of Simplified Models
- Whole catchment modelling — scoping study
- Improved methods for national spatial–temporal rainfall and evaporation modelling
- National river catchment flood frequency method using continuous simulation
- Development of estuary morphological models
- Broad-scale ecosystem impact modelling — scoping study
- Estuaries Research Programme Phase 2 — Take-up study from Phase 1
- Socio-economic impact modelling — scoping study
- Advanced hydraulic modelling tools scoping study
- Evaluation of the SIMCOAST expert system for estuary management
- Demonstration system for broad-scale modelling tools and decision support systems for flood defence planning

Flood forecasting and warning theme

- Extreme Event Recognition
- Improving dissemination of flood warnings
- Best Practice in Coastal Flood Forecasting
- Storm Scale Numerical Modelling
- Predicting extreme water levels in estuaries for flood warning
- Flood forecasting and warning — Best practice baseline review
- Reducing the Impact of flooding — Stage 1

- Rainfall Forecasting
- Real Time Modelling
- Flood Warning for Vulnerable Groups
- The Social Performance of Flood Warning Communications
- Mitigation of Climate Induced Natural Hazards (MITCH)
- Development of Flood Warning Management System
- Estimating antecedent conditions of catchment wetness
- Inclusion of organisations in flood planning and warning — Supporting activities
- Improved Flood Warning Awareness and Response in Low Probability/High Risk Flood Zones

Risk evaluation and understanding of uncertainty theme
- Absolute fixing of tide gauge benchmarks — phase II
- Risk and Uncertainty Review
- Coastal Defence Vulnerability
- Joint probability — analysis and dissemination
- Indicators of environmental change for flood and coastal defence
- Concerted action on strategic approach to data and information
- Risk evaluation of Environment Agency flood retention reservoirs
- Risk Assessment of Flood and Coastal Defence Systems for Strategic Planning
- Failure 'on demand' of Flood Defence scheme components
- Climate change impact scenarios
- Climate change impacts on flood flows in river catchments
- Performance and reliability of flood and coastal defence structures

Engineering theme
- Sand dune processes and management for flood and coastal defence
- Soft Cliffs: Prediction of Recession Rates and Erosion Control Techniques: Examples and Publication
- Low cost rock structures for beach control and coast protection

- Coastal Flooding Hazard by Wave Overtopping
- Reducing the risks of embankment failure under extreme conditions
- Coastal Flood Hazard by Wave Overtopping — Phase 2
- Design and operation of trash screens — Phase 3
- Fluvial design manual — Phase 2
- Condition monitoring and asset management of complex infrastructure systems
- Hydraulic performance of bridges and other structures at high flows — Phases 1 and 2
- Integrating buildability and improved efficiency into coastal schemes through partnering
- Reducing uncertainty in river flood conveyance — Phase 2
- Concerted Action on Operation and Maintenance of Flood and Coastal Defences
- Application of river and coastal restoration and habitat improvement techniques
- Flood Resistance of Domestic Buildings and Small Business Premises
- Temporary and Demountable Flood Defences — Phase 1
- Concerted Action on Flood and Coastal Defence Construction
- Updating Freeboard Manual
- HEC-RAS river flow model benchmarking
- Engineering Materials in River and Coastal Engineering
- Coastal and marine environmental site guide
- Coastal defence design and practice guide
- Weirs — Best practice guidance
- Source control using permeable surfaces — Hydraulic and structural performance
- Centre for Aquatic Plant Management (CAPM)

11.7.9   Further research should be carried out into all the available options for improving the flood resistance of both existing and new buildings. The aim should be to identify innovative and cost-effective solutions that will be readily adopted by the building industry.

11.8   MODEL DEVELOPMENT

11.8.1   Modelling will allow not only the testing of flood scenarios based on current catchment conditions, but also a dynamic perspective through investigation of future scenarios with various climate change and development assumptions.

11.8.2   It is important that models are be developed to match the scale and complexity of the problem. It should also be recognised that there is a distinction between the use of models for design and the use of models for operational, active risk management.

11.8.3   The significant value of historical data is recognised. However, we need to look at more innovative methods of flood estimation, including modelling, if we are to successfully manage flood risk.

11.8.4   A need has been identified to develop and further integrate hydrodynamic modelling, examining channel change and sedimentation, with hydrological sensitivity analyses to improve the accuracy of flood level estimates. This model coupling should occur at both catchment and sub-catchment scales and there is a need to pool best use in their practice.

11.8.5   Flood hydrograph forecasting is not yet being trusted by those who use it in flood emergencies in the UK. The authors recommend that current methodologies be continually refined so that state-updating from catchment sensors is employed in forecasting models to the maximum extent that brings useful performance gains.

11.8.6   The development of regional flood response models should be progressed more urgently. Although complete standardisation may be unhelpful in all cases, core concepts and algorithms should be transparent enough to perceive why differences are needed.

11.9   SKILLS SHORTAGE

11.9.1   It is the general conclusion of the authors that the appropriate technical skills are lacking within the industry, from drainage engineers in local authorities to river engineers in the Environment

Agency and skilled hydraulic specialists in universities. This lack of skills resources requires urgent attention.

11.9.2 With the increased technical demands of management, an improvement in staffing levels within the industry should be considered, particularly with regard to senior technical and managerial posts concerned with flood management. A policy is required for attracting, training and keeping staff to higher technical and management levels, with a thorough understanding of the processes involved and skills in advanced modelling techniques (hydrological and hydrodynamic).

11.9.3 It is acknowledged that frequent movement of staff within the industry as part of the staff development programme has an adverse impact on the ability of the industry to respond to flood events. Local and detailed knowledge of rivers, flood defences, hydrology and flood forecasting systems is important. The industry needs to consider how to foster technical skills without undermining promotional prospects.

11.9.4 There is a critical need to develop a structure of flood risk management that ensures sustained leadership and professional skills are available as a high priority and that all stakeholders are brought together in partnership to promote the quality of service to the community in flood risk management.

11.9.5 There is evidence that there has been a disconnection between research in universities and research in consultancies and other organisations. A partnership approach must be promoted in the future that must include university departments.

11.9.6 A review of the skills required in flood risk management is recommended and an assessment of the skills shortage that is perceived to exist.

11.10 AVAILABILITY OF DATA

11.10.1 Publicly collected primary and processed data (topographical, meteorological, hydrological and hydraulic) should be made publicly available, as is the case in the United States. This would result in improved flood risk assessment and management.

11.10.2 Ways of integrating knowledge between the disciplines of hydrology and hydraulics are required for effective flood risk management. Impetus should be given to the establishment of a good database of flood events. This should include the provision of additional flood flow measuring stations and the development of reliable stage–discharge relationships for all existing stations and key hydraulic structures. It is suggested that, as a first step, stage–discharge data and rating curves at all gauging locations should be added to the *Flood Estimation Handbook* (CEHW, 1999), as it is common to both disciplines.

11.10.3 Consideration should be given to increasing the acquisition of primary data for catchment planning purposes, including the possibility of installing new telemetered rainfall, water level and soil moisture gauges.

11.10.4 There is evidence of the under-use of data series. Analysis of flooding probability could be improved if computerisation of the UK's archive of daily rainfalls at 1000+ sites was completed.

11.10.5 There is a lack of reliable flood event data. Greater emphasis should be placed on the collection of flood data during flood events — this should be done in a way that does not add to the burden already placed upon the Environment Agency and other staff during emergencies.

11.10.6 Data should be made available by transport authorities — such as highways, railways and airports — which should commission and publish flood risk surveys of flood-prone routes or locations, especially where these can be cut for long periods (as in chalk-bourne areas) or where heavily trafficked routes are capable of being severely affected.

11.10.7 The authors recommend utilising a wider range of catchment flood forecasting and warning tools and closer coordination of Meteorological Office and Environment Agency functions in this field. This should include a review of current practice and assessment of the beneficial use of real-time monitoring to manage the operation of flood defences.

11.11   RESOURCING

11.11.1 There is a strong case for significant increases in real terms in public spending on all aspects of flood risk management, from maintenance of existing flood defence assets to provision of new flood defences to flood warning and emergency planning procedures.

11.11.2 If public expectations are to be met, increased public spending needs to be sustained over a long period and not cut back if the country enjoys some relatively flood-sparse years. A two-headed strategy is recommended.

   (*a*) In the short term, priority in any increased public spending should be directed to improving maintenance of critical flood defence assets and action to tackle flood 'hot spots'.
   (*b*) In the longer term, a clear linkage should be developed between the priorities emerging from the new catchment flood management plans and the allocation of available national funds.

11.11.3 The technical review undertaken has shown that flooding from urban drainage systems is a problem and, although the scale of such incidents is often not great, the number across the country is significant and warrants greater investment than has been made to date. Incidents such as the flooding of houses with sewage as a result of overloaded sewers are even more distressful than surface water flooding and pose a considerable health risk.

11.11.4 The same rigour should be applied to investment decisions associated with flood preparedness and response measures as those to engineered flood defences.

11.12   RESPONSIBILITY FOR FLOODING

11.12.1 The responsibility for flood risk management should be consolidated around one executive agency with enhanced supervisory powers over the various operating authorities. This agency should have resources allocated directly from the Government and have responsibility for spending prioritisation, preparation and implementation of catchment flood management plans and delivery of DEFRA's *High Level Targets for Flood and Coastal Defence* (MAFF, 1999b).

11.13 LEGISLATION

11.13.1 It is strongly recommended that current sewerage legislation is reviewed with sewer flood control in mind. The review should include an assessment of the current low levels of investment in sewer improvement to reduce flood risk and the need for a more 'joined-up' approach to the whole issue of urban drainage.

11.13.2 There has been a reluctance to accept responsibility for maintenance of sustainable urban drainage systems, which has constrained progress of these systems. This reluctance should be addressed by the Government and suitable measures taken to overcome it, if necessary by a change in the law.

11.13.3 The categorisation of watercourses into 'main river', 'ordinary watercourses' and 'critical ordinary watercourses' is arbitrary and unhelpful. It adds more confusion in the minds of the public and emphasises the divided responsibility that has been raised as a cause for concern by many of the consultees. It is recommended that the need for these definitions is reviewed in the light of calls for single-point responsibility for flood risk management.

11.13.4 It is further recommended that any responsibility for riparian drainage maintenance should be added to registered land titles. This would most readily be achieved at re-registration of a land transfer.

11.13.5 The authors recommend that all surveys for future property sales should include an assessment of likely flood risk.

11.14 CONCLUDING SUMMARY

The recommendations presented in this publication will be of little value if there are not sufficient numbers of high-quality skilled professionals available to implement them. The Institution of Civil Engineers (ICE) recognises this and will use its influence to promote the ICE as the recognised training and professional qualification body at the forefront of flood risk management and river basin engineering.

As indicated in the early sections of this book, the ICE has throughout the last century been the professional body involved in advancing the debate and introducing best practice in flood management and river basin engineering. This book is seen by the ICE as a contribution to a wider debate that must embrace the social and economic dimension of flooding and the issues of environment, land use, planning, infrastructure, development and emergency response. The debate will continue but the solution must be sustainable. With determination this can be done within the decade. We recommend we start now.

References

Abbott, M. B. and Basco, D. R. (1989). *Computational fluid dynamics — an introduction for engineers.* Longman.

Abbot, M. B., Bathurst, J. C., Cunge, J. A., O'Connell, P. E. and Rasmussen, J. (1986). An introduction to the European Hydrological System — Système Hydrologique Européen 'SHE' 2. Structure of the physically based, distributed modelling system. *Journal of Hydrology*, **87**, 61–77.

Abbott, M. B. and Refsgaard, J. C. (1996). *Distributed Hydrological Modelling.* Kluwer Academic publishers, Dordrecht.

Acreman, M. (1988). *Hydrological Data UK 1988, National River Flow Archive annual yearbook.* Institute of Hydrology, Wallingford.

Andersson, L. (1992). Improvements of runoff models — which way to go? *Nordic Hydrology*, **23**, 315–332.

Arnell, N. W. (1998). Climate change and water resources in Britain. *Climatic Change*, **39**, 83–110.

Association of British Insurers (2000). *Inland Flooding Risk — Issues Facing the Insurance Industry.*

Bailey, R. (1991). *An introduction to river management.* The Institution ofWater and Environmental Management, IWEM Booklet No. 2, pp. 1–51.

Balbanis, P., Bronstert, A., Casale, R. and Samuels, P. G. (1999). RIBAMOD, River basin modelling, management and flood mitigation — concerted action: The impact of climate change on flooding and sustainable river management. *Proceedings of the final workshop* (P. Balbanis, A. Bronstert, R. Casale and P. G. Samuels (eds)), European Commission, EUR 18287 EN, 1-404.

Bayliss, A. C. and Reed, D. W. (2001). *The use of historical data in flood frequency estimation.* Centre for Ecology and Hydrology, Report to MAFF, March, 87pp.

Becker, A. and Serban, P. (1990). Hydrological models for water resources system design and operation. *Operational Hydrology Report 34,* WMO No. 740, Geneva, Switzerland.

Bell, V. A., Carrington, D. S. and Moore, R. J. (2000). Comparison of rainfall–runoff models for flood forecasting. Part 2: Calibration and evaluation of models. *Report prepared by the Institute of Hydrology for the Environment Agency,* R&D Technical Report W242, 239pp.

Bennet, G. (1970). Bristol Floods 1968: Controlled survey of effects on health of local community disaster. *British Medical Journal,* **3**, 454–458.

Beven, K. J. (1996). A discussion of distributed hydrological modelling. In M. B. Abbot and J. C. Refsgaard (eds), *Distributed Hydrological Modelling,* Kluwer Academic Publishers, Dordrecht, The Netherlands, Chapter 13, pp. 255–295.

Beven, K. J. and Binley, A. M. (1992). The future of distributed models: model calibration and uncertainty prediction. *Hydrological Processes,* **6**, 279–298.

Beven, K. J., Kirkby, M. J., Schofield, N. and Tagg, A. F. (1984). Testing a physically-based flood forecasting model (TOPMODEL) for three UK catchments. *Journal of Hydrology,* **69**, 119–143.

Binnie (1967). *The Dee Crossing Study Phase 1.* HMSO, London.

Biswas, A. K. (1967). *Development of the Science of Hydrology to 1950 AD.* Unpublished PhD thesis, Department of Civil Engineering, University of Strathclyde, Glasgow, UK.

Biswas, A. K. and Fleming, G. (1966). Floods in Scotland: Magnitude and Frequency. *Water and Water Engineering,* June, 246–252.

British Waterways (2000). *Annual Report and Accounts 1999–2000.* British Waterways, Watford, UK.

Cabinet Office (2001). *Future of Emergency Planning in England and Wales: A Discussion Document.* Cabinet Office, London, UK.

Calver, A. and Wood, W. L. (1995). The Institute of Hydrology distributed model. In V. P. Singh (ed.), *Computer models of watershed hydrology,* Water Resources Publications, Colorado, USA, pp. 595–626.

Casale, R. (1998). Hydrological risks: analysis of recent results from EC research and technological development actions. *Environment and climate change programme,* DG-SR&D, EU.

CEH and Meteorological Office (2001) *To what degree can the October/November floods events be attributed to climate change?* CEH/Met Office, UK, published at http://www.defra.gov.uk/environ/fcd/floodingincidents/fd2304fr.pdf

CEHW (1999). *Flood Estimation Handbook* (and accompanying WINFAP-FEH software and FEH CD-ROM digital data). Centre for Hydrology and Ecology, Wallingford (formerly Institute of Hydrology).

Chambers (1981). *Chambers Twentieth Century Dictionary.* The Pitman Press, Bath.

CIRIA (1997). *Culvert Design Guide.* Construction Industry Research and Information Association, London, UK

CIRIA (2001). *Sustainable Urban Drainage Systems.* Construction Industry Research and Information Association, London, UK.

CIWEM(2001). Calming the Quaggy. *Water and Environmental Manager*, November 2001.

Cole, G. (1965). An Application of the Regional Analysis of Flood Flows. *River Flood Hydrology, Proceedings of the Symposium organized by, and held at, the Institution of Civil Engineers on Thursday, 18 March*, ICE, London, UK.

Commons Agriculture Select Committee (2001). *Flood and Coastal Defence: Follow up.* 3rd Report Session 2001–01, HC 172.

Crawford, N. H. and Linsley, R. K. (1966). Digital Simulation in Hydrology. *Stanford Watershed Model IV, TR 39*, Department of Civil Engineering, Stanford, USA.

Cunge, J. A., Holly, F. M. and Verwey, A. (1980). *Practical aspects of computational river hydraulics.* Pitman (avalable from University of Iowa, USA).

DEFRA (2001). *National Appraisal of Assets at Risk of Flooding and Coastal Erosion, including the potential impacts of Climate Change — Final Report July 2001.* Department for the Environment, Food and Rural Affairs, London, UK.

DEFRA/Environment Agency (2001). *Temporary and demountable flood defences.* Department for the Environment, Food and Rural Affairs/Environment Agency R&D project, unpublished.

Dent, J. E. (2001). *Meetings with Flood Warning Officers: Outcome, main issues and common themes arising.* Internal Note (January), Environment Agency, Bristol, UK.

Dooge, J. C. I. (1977). Problems and methods of rainfall–runoff modelling. In T. A. Ciriani, U. Maione and J. R. Wallis (eds), *Mathematical models for surface water hydrology*, Proceedings of the IBM Scientific Centre, Pisa, Italy, Wiley, pp. 71–108.

DTLR (2001). *Planning Policy Guidance Note 25, Development and Flood Risk.* Department for Transport, Local Government and the Regions, London, UK.

Environment Agency (1998). *Easter 1998 Floods, Report by the Independent Review Team to the Board of the Environment Agency* (Chairman Peter Bye). Environment Agency, Bristol, UK.

Environment Agency (2000a). *Flood defence human resources strategy.* Environment Agency, Bristol, UK.

Environment Agency (2000b). *Gainsborough Flood Alleviation Scheme — a catalyst for regeneration.* Environment Agency, Bristol, UK.

Environment Agency (2000c). *Flood Estimation Guidelines.* Environment Agency, Bristol, UK.

Environment Agency (2000d). *Fluvial Freeboard Guidance Note, Technical Report W187.* Environment Agency, Bristol, UK.

Environment Agency (2001a). *Lessons Learned: Autumn 2000 Floods.* Environment Agency, Bristol, UK.

Environment Agency (2001b). *Shrewsbury Flood Alleviation Scheme.* Environment Agency, Bristol, UK.

Environment Agency (2001c). *Design and operation of trash screens.* Environment Agency, Bristol, UK, due for publication.

Environment Agency (2001d). *Autumn 2000 Floods Review, Regional Reports.* Environment Agency, Bristol, UK.

Environment Agency (2001e). *Reducing flood risk: a framework for change.* Environment Agency, Bristol, UK.

Environment Agency (2001f). *The Leigh Barrier — The Silent Saviour.* Environment Agency, Bristol, UK.

Environment Agency (2001g). *Afflux at Bridges.* (Research project due for publication in 2002.)

European Union (2000). *Water Framework Directive* (2000/60/EC).

EUROTAS (1998). *European River Flood Occurrence and Total Risk Assessment System.* European Commission Directorate General XII Science, Research and Development, Environment and Climate, Contract Number ENV4 CT97-0535, http://www.hrwallingford.co.uk/projects/EUROTAS/

Fleming, G. (1970). Simulation of Streamflow in Scotland. *Bulletin of the International Association of Scientific Hydrology,* **XV**, No. 1(3), 53–59.

Fleming, G. (1975). *Computer Simulation Techniques in Hydrology.* Elsevier, New York, USA.

Fleming, G. and Guenin, M. (2001). *The effect of historic river engineering on flood risk: The Clyde at Pacific Quay.* Unpublished report, University of Strathclyde, Glasgow, UK.

Flood Hazard Research Centre (1999). *The Effects Of Floods: The Easter 1998 Floods in England.* Flood Hazard Research Centre Article Series No. 3/99, Middlesex University, http://www.fhrc.mdx.ac.uk/floods.pdf

Gardner, J. L. (1998). Developments in floodplain risk management: decision-making in England and Wales. In S. Fukuoka (ed.), *Floodplain risk management*, Balkema, pp. 291–306.

Garrad, P. (2001) *Identification of Flood Indicators and Trends in Flood Peaks.* Environment Agency, Bristol, UK.

Global Water Partnership (2000). Towards water security: a framework for action. *World Water Forum*, The Hague, March.

Halcrow Water (2001). *Interim Guidelines for consultation and pilot catchment studies.* For the Environment Agency/MAFF Catchment Flood Management Plans.

Haywood, J. (2001). Implementing advanced flood warning techniques. *European Flood Defence and Land Drainage Summit*, pp. 1–20.

Hempel, C. G. (1963). Explanations and predictions by covering laws. In B. Baumrin (ed.), *Philosophy of Science; the Delaware seminar*, Wiley, pp. 107–133.

HR Wallingford (2001). *Risk, Performance and Uncertainty in Flood and Coastal Defence — A Review.* HR Wallingford, Wallingford, Report SR 587.

Hulme, M. and Jenkins G. F. (1998). *Climate Change Scenarios for the United Kingdom Scientific Report.* UKCIP Technical Report 1, Climate Research Unit, Norwich, UK.

ICE (1996). *Land Drainage and Flood Defence Responsibilities.* Institution of Civil Engineers, London, UK.

ICE (2001). *Learning to Live with Rivers.* Institution of Civil Engineers, London, UK.

IPCC (2001). *Third Assessment Report: Climate Change 2001.* Cambridge University Press, Technical Summary at http://www.ipcc.ch/pub/reports.htm

Jones, D. (2001) *Personal Correspondence on odds and chance.*

Kitagawa, A. (1998). Past and recent developments of flood control in the Tone River. In S. Fukuoka (ed.), *Floodplain Risk Management*, Balkema, pp. 61–74.

Knight, D. W. (1996a). River management in the UK and the determination of the conveyance and sediment transport capacity of flood channels. *Proceedings of the International Seminar on Recent Trends of Floods and their Preventive Measures*, Hokkaido River Disaster Prevention Research Center, Sapporo, Japan, June, pp. 87–106.

Knight, D. W. (1996b). Issues and directions in river mechanics — Closure of sessions 2, 3 and 5. In T. Nakato and R. Ettema (eds), *Issues and directions in hydraulics, An Iowa Hydraulics Colloquium in honour of Professor John F. Kennedy,* Iowa Institute of Hydraulic Research, Iowa, USA, Balkema, pp. 435–462.

Knight, D. W. and Abril, B. (1996). Refined calibration of a depth-averaged model for turbulent flow in a compound channel. *Proceedings of the Institution. of Civil Engineers, Water, Maritime and Energy,* **118**, No. 3, Sept., Paper No. 11017, pp. 151–159.

Knight, D. W. and Shiono, K. (1996). River channel and floodplain hydraulics. In Anderson, Walling and Bates (eds), *Floodplain Processes,* Chapter 5, J. Wiley, pp. 139–181.

Kondo, T. (1998). Requirements for crisis management in flood control plans. In S. Fukuoka (ed.), *Floodplain risk management*, Balkema, pp. 13–35.

Lamb, H. H. (1995). *Climate, History and the Modern World.* Routledge, pp. 433.

Lambert, A. (1972). Catchment models based on iso-functions. *Journal of the Institution of Water Engineers*, **26**, 413–422.

Lunan, N. (2001). Flood Event Mitigation — The American Way. Presented at *After the Flood: Lessons Learned from the Scottish Experience*, 26 October, Perth. See http://www.caber.org.uk/events/flood/docs/lunan_paper.doc

MacDougall, K. A. (1999). *Groundwater Contamination: A Risk Based Approach.* Unpublished PhD thesis, Department of Civil Engineering, University of Strathclyde, Glasgow, UK.

MAFF (1993). *Strategy for Flood and Coastal Defence in England and Wales.* Ministry of Agriculture, Fisheries and Food/Welsh Office, HMSO, London, UK.

MAFF (1997). *Interim Guidance for the Strategic Planning and Appraisal of Flood and Coastal Defence Schemes.* Ministry of Agriculture, Fisheries and Food, London, UK.

MAFF (1999a). *Flood and Coastal Defence Project Appraisal Guidance.* Ministry of Agriculture, Fisheries and Food, London, UK.

MAFF (1999b). *High Level Targets for Flood and Coastal Defence.* Ministry of Agriculture, Fisheries and Food, London, UK.

MAFF (1999c). *Flood and Coastal Research and Development.* Report of the Advisory Committee, Ministry of Agriculture, Fisheries and Food, London, UK.

MAFF (1999d). *Flood and Coastal Defence Project Appraisal Guidance, Approaches to Risk.* Ministry of Agriculture, Fisheries and Food, London, UK.

MAFF (2000). *National Appraisal of Assets at risk from flooding and coastal erosion — final Report June 2000.* Ministry of Agriculture, Fisheries and Food, London, UK.

MAFF/Environment Agency (2000). *Flood and Coastal Defence R&D programme — thematic structure.* Ministry of Agriculture, Fisheries and Food, London, UK.

Magness, J. (2001). The October 2000 Floods. Presented at *Flooding and Insurance in Autumn 2000 and beyond*, 28 June, ABI, London, UK.

Marsh, T. J. (2001) Climate change and hydrological stability: a look at long-term trends in south eastern Britain. *Weather,* **56**, 319–326

McEwan, I. K. and Fukuoka, S. (2002). *Flow and sediment transport in two-stage channels.* IAHR Monograph, Balkema.

Miller, J. B. (1997). *Floods: people at risk, strategies for prevention.* DHA/97/107, United Nations, Geneva.

Milne, J. (2001). The ABI's medium term position. Presented at *Flooding and Insurance in Autumn 2000 and beyond*, 28 June, ABI, London, UK.

Moore, R. J. (1999). Real-time flood forecasting systems: perspectives and prospects. In R. Casale and C. Margottini (eds), *Floods and Landslides: Integrated Risk Assessment*, Chapter 11, Springer-Verlag, pp. 147–189.

Moore, R. J. and Bell, V. A. (2000). Comparison of rainfall–runoff models for flood forecasting. Part 1: Literature review of models. *Report prepared by the Institute of Hydrology for the Environment Agency,* R&D Technical Report W241, 94pp.

Mott MacDonald Ltd (2000). *Flood forecasting and warning good practice baseline review. Part 1 — Existing practice and Part 2 — Recommendations.* R&D Technical Report, W5C-013.

Mulvaney, T. J. (1850). *The Use of Self-registering Rain and Flood Gauges in Making Observations of the Relations of Rainfall and of Flood Discharges in a Given Catchment.* Transactions, Institution of Civil Engineers of Ireland, Vol. 4, Part 2.

Nakato, T. and Ettema, R. (1996). *Issues and directions in hydraulics, An Iowa Hydraulics Colloquium in honour of Professor John F. Kennedy.* Iowa Institute of Hydraulic Research, Iowa, USA, Balkema.

Nash, J. E. (1957). *The form of the instantaneous unit hydrograph.* IASH Publication Number 45, 3, pp. 114–121.

National Audit Office (2001). *Inland Flood Defence.* Report by the Controller and Auditor General HC 299, Session 2000/1, March 2001.

NCE (2001). Debate: Homes Built on Flood Plains. *New Civil Engineer*, 22 November, p. 17.

NERC (1975). *Flood Studies Report.* Natural Environment Research Council, London, UK.

NERC (1997). *Hydrometric Register and Statistics.* Natural Environment Research Council, London, UK.

O'Connell, P. E. (1991). A historical perspective. In D. S. Bowels and P. E. O'Connell (eds), *Recent Advances in the Modelling of Hydrologic Systems*, Kluwer Academic publishers, pp. 3–30.

O'Connor, K. M. (1995). River flow forecasting: the Galway experience. *Proceedings of the Symposium on River Flow Forecasting and Disaster Relief*, Haikou City, China.

O'Connor, K. M. (1997). Advanced course/workshop on river flow forecasting. *Proceedings of the 7th International Workshop*, National University of Ireland, Galway, Eire.

OFWAT (1999). *The 1999 Periodic Review — Final Determination. Future Water and Sewerage Charges 2000 to 2005.* Office of Water Services, UK.

OFWAT (2001). *Levels of Service for the Water Industry in England and Wales.* Office of Water Services, UK.

Osborne T. J., Hulme, M., Jones, P. D. and Basnett, T. A. (2000). Observed trends in the daily intensity of UK precipitation. *International Journal of Climatology,* **20**, 347–364.

Perrin, C., Michel, C. and Andreassian, V. (2001). Does a large number of parameters enhance model performance? Comparative assessment of common catchment model structures on 429 catchments. *Journal of Hydrology*, **242**, 275–301.

Reed, D. W. (1999). Overview. *Flood Estimation Handbook*, Vol. 1, Institute of Hydrology, Wallingford.

Refsgaard, J. C. (1997). Validation and inter-comparison of different updating procedures for real time forecasting. *Nordic Hydrology*, **28**, 65–84.

RIBAMOD (1999). RIBAMOD River basin modelling, management and flood mitigation — concerted action: The impact of climate change on flooding and sustainable river management. In P. Balbanis, A. Bronstert,

R. Casale and P. G. Samuels (eds), *Proceedings of the final workshop*, European Commission, EUR 18287 EN, 1–404.

Robinson, M. and Rycroft, D.W. (1999). The impact of drainage on streamflow. In R. W. Skaggs and J. van Schilfgaarde (eds), *Agricultural Drainage*, American Society of Agronomy, Inc., Wisconsin, USA, pp. 767–800.

Robson, A. J. and Reed, D. W. (1999). Statistical procedures for flood frequency estimation. *Flood Estimation Handbook*, Vol. 3, Institute of Hydrology, Wallingford.

Robson, A. J., Jones, T. K., Reed, D. W. and Bayliss, A. C. (1998) A study of national trend and variation in UK floods. *International Journal of Climatology*, **18**, 165–182

Sadler, J. P. and Grattan, J. P. (1999). Volcanoes as agents of past environmental change. *Global and Planetary Change*, **21**, 181–196.

Sellin, R. H. J., Ervine, D. A and Willetts, B. B. (1993). Behaviour of meandering two stage channels. *Proceeedings of the Institution of Civil Engineers, Water, Maritime and Energy*, **101**, 99–111.

Serban, P. and Askew, A. J. (1991). Hydrological forecasting and updating procedures. In F. H. M. van de Ven, G. Gutknecht, D. P. Loucks and K. A. Salewicz (eds), *Hydrology for the water management of large river basins*, Proceedings of the Vienna Symposium, August, IAHS publication No. 201, pp. 357–369.

Shamseldin, A. Y. (1996). *Fundamental studies in rainfall–runoff modelling*. PhD thesis, The National University of Ireland, Galway.

Shamseldin, A. Y., Ahmed, E. N. and O'Connor, K. M. (2001). Comparison of different forms of the multi-layer feed-forward neural network method for river flow forecast combination. *Journal of Hydrology and Earth System Sciences* (to be published).

Shamsen, A. Y., O'Connor, K. M. and Liang, G. C. (1997). Methods for combining the outputs of different rainfall–runoff models. *Journal of Hydrology*, **197**, 203–229.

Shaw, E. M. (1994). *Hydrology in practice*. Chapman and Hall.

Sherman, L. K. (1932). Streamflow from rainfall by the unit-graph method. *Engineering News Record*, **108**, 501–505.

Simons, D. B. (1992). Future trends and needs in hydraulics. *Journal of Hydraulic Engineering, ASCE*, **118**, No. 12, December, 1607–1620.

Singh, V. P. (1995). *Computer models of watershed hydrology*. Water Resources Publications, Colorado.

Tickle, K. S. (1996). Stochastic hydraulics '96. *Proceedings of the 7th IAHR International Symposium,* Queensland, Australia, Balkema.

Todini, E. (1993). Flood forecasting models. *Proceedings of the International Workshop on River Flood Forecasting*, 17–29 September, Beijing, China.

Todini, E. (1998). Rainfall–runoff modelling — past and present. *Journal of Hydrology*, **100**, 341–352.

UKCIP (1998). *Climate Change Impacts in Scotland: Workshop Report* (including contributions from NW England and East Anglia). UK Climate Impacts Programme. See http://www.eci.ox.ac.uk/UK%20Climate%20Impacts-%20Programme/Scottish_Workshop.html

UKCIP (2000). *Climate Change: Assessing the Impacts — Identifying the Responses.* Environmental Change Institute, Oxford University, pp.160. See summary at http://www.eci.ox.ac.uk/UK%20Climate%20Impacts%20-Programme/short-report.html

Warwickshire County Council (1998). *A Flood of Claims.* Warwickshire County Council Trading Standards, UK.

Watanabe, Y. (1998). Flood control countermeasures in Japan. In S. Fukuoka (ed.), *Floodplain Risk Management*, Balkema, pp. 39–53.

Webster, P. (1998). *Rainfall boundary conditions for hydrological design.* PhD thesis, The University of Birmingham.

Webster, P. and Ashfaq, M. (2001). Comparison of UK flood event characteristics with design guidelines. *Proceedings of the Institution of Civil Engineers, Water, Maritime and Energy* (in press).

White, W. R. (2000). Rivers in flood. Special paper for *Towards water security: a framework for action.* World water Forum, The Hague, March.

Woolhiser, D. A. (1996). Search for physically based runoff model — a hydrologic El Dorado? *Journal of Hydraulic Engineering, ASCE*, **122**, No. 3, March, 122–129.

World Meteorological Organization (WMO) (1992). *Simulated real-time inter-comparison of hydrological models.* Operational Hydrology Report 38, WMO No. 779, Geneva.

Ye, W., Bates, B. C., Viney, N. R., Sivapalan, M. and Jakeman, A. J. (1997). Performance of conceptual rainfall–runoff models in low-yielding ephemeral catchments. *Water Resources Research*, **33**, No. 1, January, 153–166.

Further reading

Beven, K. J. (2001). *Rainfall–runoff modelling* (just published).

Environment Agency (2000). *Flood Warning Investment Strategy.* Environment Agency, Bristol, UK.

Environment Agency (2001). *An environmental vision: the Environment Agency's contribution to sustainable development.* Environment Agency, Bristol, UK.

Environment Agency (2001). *Implementing Advanced Flood Warning Techniques.* Environment Agency, Bristol, UK.

Guganesharajah, K. (2001), *Development of computational hydraulic and water quality models for rivers, estuaries, reservoirs and aquifers.* PhD thesis, University of Surrey.

Hadley Centre (2000). *Climate Change — An Update of Recent Research from the Hadley Centre,* http://www.metoffice.com/research/hadleycentre/pubs/

Hulme, M., Jenkins, G. J., Lu, X., Turnpenny, T. D., Mitchell, T. D., Jones, R. G., Lowe, J., Murphy, J. M., Hassell, D. Boorman, P., McDonald, R. and Hill, S. (2002). *Climate Change Scenarios for the United Kingdom: The UKCIP02 Scientific Report.* Tyndall Centre for Climate Change Research, School of Environmental Sciences, University of East Anglia, Norwich, for DEFRA, 120pp.

POSTnote 151 (2000). *Floods and rains.* December 2000.

SCARM (2000). *Floodplain Management in Australia, SCARM Report 73.* CSIRO Publishing, Australia.

Sussex Express (2001). *Baker calls for action on floods.* 13 July.

WRc plc (1995). *Sewers for Adoption,* fourth edition. WRc plc, UK.

Index

Page numbers in italics refer to illustrations.